<u>Biography</u>

Marte King is an Urban Author whose subject area entails his personal struggles in the trying streets of America, as well as in our controversial prison systems. He writes for the purpose of educating the American populous with the hard truths of what goes on out of the public's view. He is in Recovery and is striving to make a positive change in the world as he has made within himself.

Fruition

If your experiences would benefit anybody,
give them to someone.

Florence Nightingale

IN MEMORY OF MY FATHER

DEXTER DAVIS

OCTOBER 2, 1954 - APRIL30, 2010

Acknowledgments

All Praise are due to God, through all things are possible.

I dedicate this book to my mother, Sabrina King, grandmother, Barbara King and my sons, Marquan and Bukhari.

I give special thanks to my fiancé, My Queen, Kimberly Nicholson who, for the last three years, has been my backbone.

I would also like to thank Mrs. Laura Griffin-Greenwood, my mentor who shares my vision for RePENT.

I am thankful to Mr. Frank Scannapieco for his content editing.

Last, but not lease, thanks to my sister-in-law, Dana Nicholson, for her help in the interior editing.

"RePent"

Because The Time Is At Hand . . . . .

CONTENTS

Introduction .... *vii*

Becoming A Palliative Care Volunteer 1

Mr. Omar Williams 9

Mr. Godsby 25

Mr. White 32

Mr. Goh 53

The Colonel 75

Mr. Krochmelnik 81

Mr. McKenzie 89

Mr. Rivera 97

Mr. Williford 121

Mr. Sumpter 139

Ms. Islam 142

Green Eyes 158

Najiullah Musihuden 170

Ivory "One Round" Johnson 177

Introduction

Fruition is a memoir of my experiences while volunteering in a hospice program at South Woods State Prison. The program is named Palliative Care, and is modeled after a program that evolved in Louisiana's infamous Angola Penitentiary. This program was developed partially through necessity, because the majority of inmates in this population are terminally ill, and will never go home.

With our economy having dwindled under the Bush administration; it is the upright, hard working, tax-paying and law abiding citizens who are struggling -- with might and mien - to provide even the minimal of medical coverage for their families. Likewise, elderly Americans, who have paid their debts to society, are now facing the reality of not having Social Security Benefits. These being the cases, imagine how horrific it is for those who are considered the scourge of society, i.e. the incarcerated. It's **HORRIBLE**! In America, we have human beings left to rot with less compassion than we show our pets. They have been banished and dumped in dark, dank, under-ventilated rooms with the stench of death looming overhead like a mushroom cloud.

Throughout the State of New Jersey, terminally ill male prisoners are transferred to the Emergency Care Unit (E.C.U.) at South Woods, under the guise of benevolence, when in actuality it is for nothing more than fiscal prudence. E.C.U. is clean, well-lit, well-ventilated and grossly understaffed. So, while the rooms were pristine, many of the guys who were bedridden were not.

Yet, despite the stereotypes of prisoners being subhuman beasts, lacking of compassion, predisposed to violence, lacking empathy, and devoid of humaneness, a stunning and astonishing flower has taken root. Dostoyevsky said, "The true measure of a society's progress is gauged by its prisons." If this is the case, Palliative Care is an undeniable testimony of the innate goodness that dwells in the spirit of us all.

Would-be volunteers for the program are first screened for institutional infractions, and then evaluated by the mental health department, including an exam specifically designed to determine one's predisposition as a sex offender. No Tree Jumpers (Sex Offenders) are permitted into the E.C.U. because of the proximity and interaction with female nurses and staff. Once accepted as a candidate, you have to complete a comprehensive training course administered by CMS. The Program has been the subject of several local newspaper articles. One wrote: PALLIATIVE CARE: Inmates counting the number of days while helping those whose days are numbered.

This was the first time I had been in the news and didn't have WANTED posted above my picture! And you know what? It felt good. In a society filled with *egocentricity, self-absorption and outright selfishness, it feels good to be of service, and to be granted the opportunity to be self-less. To me, Palliative Care is a blessing. Actually, it's a double blessing, because I have gained more from my patients than I could ever have given them.*

It is my sincerest intention to shed a different light on the incarcerated by sharing my world. We are Americans, too. Well, most of us. We are your sons, brothers, uncles, cousins, and fathers. We have made some mistakes in life; some more than others, but none-the-less, are still imperfect human beings and children of a Power Greater than ourselves, deserving to be treated with dignity and respect. I also wish to convey some of the inspirational insights imparted upon me from my interacting with these men who are not only facing the harsh realities of impending death, but are also facing the fact that they are or will be dying behind these walls. If you find yourself laughing from time to time, please don't feel bad, I intended to accomplish that as well.

My Daily Affirmation

A real Man accepts responsibility for his own actions, and learns from his mistakes and the mistakes of others.

A real Man, being responsible, responds to adversity while an animal reacts.

And the difference between reacting and responding is the process of thinking.

What lead me to become a Palliative Care Volunteer?

In 2003, while in the law library preparing campaign letters soliciting assistance to help pay for a college correspondence course that I wanted to take through Ohio University's CPI program, I overheard a paralegal talking about Palliative Care. He said, in a sarcastic way, "We have a lot of Muslim brothers dying over there, but no Muslim brothers stepping up to help." I felt so ashamed because he was absolutely correct. I am a strong, able bodied Muslim and immediately offered my services. I applied for the program several times, but never received a response. I was determined, however, not to let any stumbling block get in my way, and would apply as many times as it would take for me to get into Palliative Care.

Meanwhile, I continued my letter writing campaign regarding the Ohio University CPI program. I wrote and rewrote everyone from Oprah to George Bush. Why not? I shared my dreams and visions with a few individuals who were closest to me and they laughed in my face. This did hurt, however, I remained steadfast and optimistic, refusing to let other's lack of vision discourage me. I'll tell you what; I have been disheartened a few times when I would receive stacks of letters back that had RETURN TO SENDER stamped with the big red finger pointing to my name, especially since it was the only mail

I was getting at the time. Still, I continued to forge forward. Their ridicule became my fuel.

In the process of drafting letters to fit a range of personalities that explained who I am and why you should give me your money, I began to recognize that I possessed a small talent for writing. After overhearing a few of the younger brothers go on- and- on over these "Hood" urban thrillers, and reading one for myself, I decided to write one that would give a little substance, a lot of food for thought along with the action of the streets. So even if I didn't get into school, the experience would be an asset.

(Look for 'One Mann Team' in a bookstore near you)

I continued to write my campaign letters. I wrote the NAACP, Muhammad Ali, Maya Angelou, Magic Johnson, Black Churches, White Churches, Masjids of all sorts and Synagogues. I was determined, and my determination finally paid off when a brother from a Masjid in Trenton gave me $1,000 to begin college. The feeling I had when I received his letter made all those "return to sender's" inconsequential. This donation enabled me to take two classes, Business Administration and Communications; both of which, I learned a great deal from.

To better understand the extent of my struggles, you need to know and feel where I was in my personal and spiritual development before my acceptance into Palliative

Care. Thus, I am going to share some of the conditions that I lived under just prior to my acceptance.

I was just beginning to get into a comfortable place in my bid. I had the top paying job, $3.10 a day, (and I wouldn't work fast food because they paid minimum wage), my ex-wife (the only woman I had ever loved) was back once again, I'm in college and I'm in a Media Arts class with a great teacher and the police finally recognize me enough to stop harassing me every time I walked down the compound. To be in prison, I'm good!

One evening, about halfway through the Month of Ramadan of 2003, right after I had broken my fast and was preparing myself for prayer, the locking device for my door turned on and off several times. This is a way of letting you know that the officer wants you at the desk for something. This was odd because we were all locked down for count. Of course I grew paranoid. I've seen too many things happen to prisoners not to feel that way. I looked out the window of my door to see what was going on.

It was Ms. W. Once I saw her smiling face I felt more at ease. But I also remembered that my down falls often revolved around women. She's got thick bow legs, a small waist, an upside down heart shaped booty and she works out regularly to stay in tip top shape; just like I like it.

Religiously, I understand the vices of fornication and adultery.

Theoretically, I understand the social ill of promiscuity.

I understand that it begins with what we allow into our sights so I don't look at pornography, and have even gone so far as to delete the Spanish channel on my T.V. (Caliente' is too hot for me.)

Nevertheless, though I have come very far, I do still struggle, and Ms. W. is definitely one of my losing battles.

In a prison filled with women -- many of whom are just as lonely as we are, who have no husband/man, or are unhappily involved with someone they are sharing -- the extent of my struggles are far greater than you would imagine.

I opened the door with my wife-beater on; (i.e. Tank top T-shirt) water was glistening over my face and arms from performing ablution for prayer.

"Do you want me?" I asked

"Yes" she answered, with a cute little smile.

"Can you turn this microwave on for me?"

I came out and headed straight to the dayroom, afraid that if I looked at her she may read my thoughts. I just stared at the incandescent light reflecting off of the freshly waxed floors. I passed the telephones and it felt eerie because nobody else was around.

4

Six-two-left is on the second floor. The dayroom that the microwave is in is partially encased in Plexiglas (like the side of a greenhouse) and is facing a tree line that is in the back of the prison. The leaves of the trees were changing to shades of orange, red, and brown and I would often marvel at GOD'S tapestry early in the mornings before everyone was up.

At night, the glass reflected the light from inside the dayroom. While adjusting the microwave to the appropriate setting, I struggled not to look at her image through the windows reflective powers.

As if she were listening to my inner conversation, she had the nerve to ask me, in her sweet little voice, while looking at me with soft brown eyes, "Do you think I'm getting fat?" and twisted her booty in my direction!

All I could do is look her in the face, briefly, with an expression that said, "You gotta be kidding me!", and run out the room.

I seek refuge in (GOD) the Lord of the Rising Sun,

From the evil of what He has created.

And from the evil of darkness as it overspreads.

And from the evil of those who practice secret arts.

And from the envier as he envies.

This must have been an omen, because next day some dummy addresses a letter to Internal Affairs claiming that the housing unit officer is going to be killed.

5

Everybody on that block with influence was immediately moved. It seems like whenever things are starting to go my way, BAM, right in the kisser. I'm honestly wondering if somebody put a hex on me.

I was moved from Phase III and sent to Phase II, which was in a totally different part of the prison. The worst part about it is that I would not be able to complete the Media Arts, the best program South Woods has to offer. They have actual T.V. cameras and editing systems. For all intents and purposes, it's an actual studio. On top of that, the teacher was phenomenal. His name was Mr. Morgan. He was one of those teachers that truly cared, and for the time period that I was in his presence, he was my mentor. He was a good Christian brother who was open minded enough to relate to spiritual principles without getting caught up in religious dogma and his example has helped me to become a better Man. Mr. Morgan, you are an excellent example of Black Manliness and I thank you.

My example of Black Womanhood, for honorable mention, is Ms. Lustenberg. She was a dignified older lady of intelligence and culture. She has been all over the world and speaks several languages. Her looks put women half her age to shame. Our interactions were much more limited than the ones I had with Mr. Morgan because I wasn't in her class. But when we did speak, her words were filled with understanding and encouragement. And though she is an African American Lady, color of any shade feels too constricting in her presence.

I put all of my possessions inside a plastic laundry cart and headed down the compound to Phase II. About halfway there I was hit with a torrential downpour. I hoped this wasn't a sign of what was to come.

Phase II, 4-1-right. There's an African American woman who's the tier cop, and she's a piece of work! During count, she would put up card board boxes in the windows of her office so nobody could see what she and the Sgt. were doing; but of course, everybody knew.

I walked to the desk, soaking wet, and waited for the officer to tell me which cell to go to. She started running down how she runs her unit, and that she will respect me as long as I respect her, and then all of the sudden she looks over to the shower area and starts screaming, "I know I don't see two sets of feet in that shower!"

There's one shower downstairs that was extra large for people who are wheelchair bound. Come to find out, it wasn't two people in the shower, it was three! One guy was standing on the security chair for the handicap. I was disgusted.

"When y'all nasty M. F.'s get out of there I better have some Newports sitting on my desk."

She slammed her hand on the desk for emphasis and then turned back around as if nothing was happening out of the norm. I guess that occurrence threw off her train of thought because she started telling me about this big dude, serving a LIFE sentence, who held a homosexual captive in his room as a Sex Slave.

She giggled as she remembered the scene in her mind and continued by telling me that the boy was so afraid that when she came by for count he held up a sign that said 'HELP'.

Then, she looked at my information on the transfer paper, which includes how much time I have to serve and said, "If you want a special guest moved in with you... we can work something out," and smiled like the Cheshire Cat.

If I were 'Homey da Clown' I would have wound up a sock filled with sand and hit her in the head! "Uh-ah, Homey don't play dat!"

The one bright side of being on Phase II was being reunited with Mr. Williams

And which of the Favors of your Lord will you deny?

Mr. Omar Williams

July 10, 2004

Mr. Williams had been locked up about 20 years or so when he and I first met. He was one of those old heads that was well respected by fellow prisoner and officers alike. He was tall, about 6'2", jet black, with a slim build, and weighed about 180. His aureole like, shimmery soft, silver-grey, three inch afro laid on his head akin to the halo of a seventeenth century artisan. When he smiled his entire face lit up and his legs were as bowed as Scatman Caruthers. He walked with a cane that was once the root of a mighty tree. When he came towards me I didn't know if he wanted to hit me with his stick or play a game of 'Kick da Can'! And his gait was proud, erect, and as dignified as a Black Civil War Soldier. In his eyes was a look that you rarely find in Black men anymore; a look that you may have to find in an old picture of first generation Freedmen to understand. A look that said, "Yes, I'm a Sharecropper, a Shoeshine, a Ditch Digger, a Garbage Man, or even a convicted Felon, nevertheless, **I AM A MAN!**"

He and I first met at the Jumu'ah services on Phase III. I was one of those dudes who greeted everyone as they came through the door of the chapel. Shaking hands and giving hugs like I was running for public office.

9

One Friday, Dr. Yusef, our Imam ran into some difficulties and couldn't make it and I was instructed to deliver the sermon. Ten minutes beforehand!

For those of you who don't know, public speaking can easily become a nightmare, even when you are fully prepared. Imagine what it's like when it's impromptu.

The moment I stood up in front of the podium, my freshly shaved head began perspiring like a crack-head with a kilo of coke. My heart was beating so hard I could feel it in my throat. This made it even more so difficult to swallow the cup of water I had just poured in my mouth.

What do I say?

What do I do?

What am I doing up here!

Scanning the legion of faces in the audience, I could practically read some of their minds. Some eagerly awaited and appeared genuinely excited to hear what I had to say. While others menacingly stared, waiting to mentally record the slightest mistake.

When Mr. Williams and I established eye contact, his pearly white smile contrasted so sharply with his dark complexion that it caught my attention slightly longer. He nodded his silver halo as if granting me approval, and I was finally able to swallow the water that was now lukewarm. At that instant, Mr. Williams became the father that I never knew, my grandfather-- who was the

10

only man I ever loved, and Mr. Nelon -- my sixth grade teacher at Kenmore Elementary who taught me more than all the teachers I have ever had, rolled up into one. He gave me exactly what I needed to proceed.

It's a trip. Many brothers enjoyed the service and commented on the topic, but to be honest with you, I haven't a clue as to what the topic was much less what I said. Whatever it was it didn't come from me.

The staple diets in prisons are extremely starchy foods. White breads, rice, potatoes, and oodles of noodles. As a result, a disproportionally high amount of men who have been incarcerated for a length of time suffer from some form of diabetes.

Mr. Williams was no exception. He had to go to have a dialysis twice a week. Every time he returned, he could barely move for at least 24 hours. It was as if they were, while removing the impurities from his blood, taking small pieces of his spark, his spirit, his soul.

Because he was so weak, I would often cook and clean his room for him. In exchange, he would enlighten me with his humor, insights, and wisdom. He could get a little bossy at times, but I didn't mind. I just kind of put myself in his shoes and imagined I'd likely be even more cantankerous. Some of the brothers who looked up to me even commented at times that Mr. Williams is 'sonning' me. (Treating me like I'm his little son.) To have said that about someone unworthy I may have been ready to fight. I still have a lot of that left in me! However, Mr. Williams was more of a father to me than my own. Plus, I recognized how the devil uses peer pressure to try and prevent you from doing something good. I humbled myself to the service of this old man like Daniel-son and Mr. Meyagi, wax on wax off, and unintentionally, showed by actions, respect of our elders to the younger brothers. Teaching them that showing reverence and compassion towards your elders does not diminish ones Manhood.

"Brother...come here for a second."

"What's up Mr. Williams?"

"Take the metal hot pot." By now he had pushed it in front of me.

"Go in my room and get six raw eggs." He held up six fingers

"Go back to your room and fry us up some eggs. Make mine over medium." And then he started to walk away.

"Man, how in the heck am I supposed to fry eggs in a hot pot?" Smiling a bit, thinking he was being facetious.

"Listen Brother, heat some butter on the bottom of the hot pot and fry the eggs like it was in a pan. It might take you 5 minute. If I do it, it will only take two. That's because I'm smarter than you."

I just looked at him, amazed at his audacity.

"You see son, you might know a little history but I know more than you. You might be able to write but I write better than you. You might know more Arabic than me but I know more Islam," and started to walk away.

"Man, what does that have to do with frying some dag on eggs in a hot-pot!"

Paying my frustration absolutely no mind, he turned back around and caught me with a right open handed hook that landed on top of my bald head and continued, "and I can fight!"

We both cracked up laughing and I did as I was told. Fifteen minutes later, we had fried egg sandwiches. I got so good that I opened up shop and began selling them.

I began to notice the same guys that made slick remarks about Mr. Williams "sonning" me were soon greasing his scalp and running errands as well. Infringing upon my quality time!

His condition got worse and he had to go to the hospital again; which he hated! When he returned, they moved him to another tier. I was sad because I felt like a member of my family had been taken.

I saw him at Friday Prayer and I told him about getting a letter of acceptance from Palliative Care, and that I was scheduled to begin training soon. He encouraged me to do it. He had heard about the program and believed I could be of benefit to the brothers. By now, my schedule was so full that I didn't see how I could give up the time to do it, but I went to the classes anyway.

We had to attend three days of training and on my last day, while heading to the E.C.U., I saw Mr. Williams. He was being pushed in a wheelchair and looked much older than the last time I had seen him. He looked uncared for. His hair was un-groomed and it had lost its shine. It was dingy gray and his skin was dull and dusty black. His clothes weren't any better; wrinkled and soiled as if he had slept in them for a week and his posture was uncharacteristically slumped over.

We greeted each other and, because some pipes were busted on the compound, we were both corralled into the administration building until some specialized heavy duty truck entered the gates. This was cool with me because it gave me the opportunity to converse with my long lost father.

It was difficult for me to mask my emotions as I looked into his decaying face. He looked up at me with a small flicker of life still lightly glimmering in his eyes and somberly uttered, "Listen here son, and let me tell you something."

His voice was so weak that I had to lean in close to understand what he was saying. I smelled a pungent aroma; the Stench of Death. It's an indescribable scent that, instinctually, I knew did not come directly from his body.

14

"Brother, I've had my eyes on you for a long time, longer than you think. You're a good young man with a good heart and you're doing a lot of good deeds. But let me tell you something."

The guy who was pushing his wheelchair noticed our closeness, and though he could likely hear ever word we were saying, he stepped over a bit to give us a semblance of privacy.

"You can do all the good deeds in the world, but when it's time to go, it ain't gonna make no difference."

For a brief moment, the life came back into him and I thought he was going to get up out of the chair.

"You may think you are prepared for death, but you will never accomplish this." He then slumped back down.

"When the Angel of Death comes to snatch your soul and you can taste the Inevitable, all that stuff you did goes out the window!"

Then he reached his hand out and I held it.

"Let me tell you something!" He squeezed tightly adding emphasis to his point. "I've tasted Death, and once you a tasted it, you ain't gonna want no more. Once its bitterness fills your mouth you are going to appreciate every breath you have ever taken. You are going to cherish every breath you are taking now, and you are gonna long for just one more."

15

Then he looked at me for a second and it felt as if a message was being conveyed from all of my ancestors who endured unspeakable hardships just for me to be here.

"Just because you're doing time doesn't mean you are not living, not learning, not growing. Take advantage of your time, no matter where you are, because TIME... is a terrible thing to waste."

That was the last conversation he and I had. He died the next day.

May GOD make your grave spacious and full of light until the Day of Judgment. (Ameen)

Security Breaches

Lives desperately hanging in the balance -- while talents slip into the darkness - - where the lawless sets the agenda for the day. Cause what you think and what you say can bring you to the brink of physical destruction so we who know now present our discussions under the disguise of mental decay.

Wayward souls pushed south for their Fruition in the iceman's woods. To him good - but strange fruit are gathered while his bastardly way take root in hot pursuit of energy that is not his - and by law must return to the essence. Reminiscent of that missing link that teaches - what - and not how to think.

One soul strategically sent to document that last moments of men discarded like Tuesday's trash. Assimilated laughs that befriends betrayed souls, which further enslaves and entrenches defined roles, who decided to give as well as roll with the punches. Friends who appeared to mysteriously fade into obscurity now pierce the corporate veil in the form of Marte' King – Breaching the Iceman's security.

TONE: *Rahway Prison Poet*

August 4, 2004

When I finished training there wasn't much to do because we had more volunteers than patients. I would go to E.C.U., every day, just for the walk. As I ventured out of the inside compounds gate, I could feel my lungs expand, my spirits livened, and I reveled from the semblance of freedom. The grounds of the main compound have decorous patches of flower beds and a neatly manicured lawn. From this vantage point, South Woods looks more like a military base than a prison. Sometimes I would take the long way back just to enjoy the scenery, inhale the fragrance, and imagine walking with my sons through the park. Play catch or wrestling with them in the grass.

As I walk through the double door entrance of E.C.U., and enter the narrow corridor leading to the front desk, I'm blinded by the refracted rays of a fledgling sun bursting through the courtyard window at the end of the hall. Its light surrounds, engulfs, and encompasses, giving on the sense that one is approaching a space unconfined by razor wire and steel. A place where angelic voices fall akin to Chopin's 'Raindrop' and softly splash upon my head, perform ablution on my thirsty earthen skin and warm my ear lobes with ambiguous chantings upon exotic tongues. A language, so exotic, that only my heart understands.

18

I seek refuge in (GOD) the Lord of the Rising Sun.

From the evil of what He created.

And from the evil of darkness as it overspreads.

From the evil of those who practice secret arts

And from the evil of the envious one as he envies.

"Mr. King"

"Mr. King"

"Mis-ter KING!

My calm scene was brought to a screeching halt by a voice in a tone far from exotic.

"Boy do you hear me calling you?"

It was Ms. Johnson. I had checked her before about calling me Boy, but I'm not going to let her ruin my morning. She was standing halfway down the hall in front of the elevator. There are only two floors in E.C.U. The elevators are for people carried out in wheelchairs and stretchers.

She was wearing an all white dress with sparkling shimmies that was loose fitting and covered most of the undesirable parts while accentuating her legs and cleavage. I guess she is feeling herself today. Or she's going to an awards show after work.

She was standing in front of the elevator with her hands on her hips, and then she grimaced, and raised her left hand to block the blinding rays of the sun. Each of her

19

fat little freshly manicured fingers bore gold rings whose fake diamonds glittered like disco balls.

"Mr. King, I was..."

All of a sudden a young Spanish nurse's aide appeared; wearing virtually transparent all white scrubs that displayed her dark purple thong and gave a hint of her honey brown derriere, netting my gaze as she gayfully passed.

"Buenos Dias." She said like a Spanish Angel.

I seek refuge in the Lord of the Rising Sun.

From the evil of the created things...

Ms. Johnson, Ms. Johnson popped me upside my head and said, "Boy! What's wrong with you?"

"Nothing, I was just uh... thinking about uh..."

"You don't have to tell me what you were thinking about with your nasty self. I can read your mind."

I guess she forgot all about catching the elevator because she just turned around and said, "Meet me in my office in ten minutes."

As the click of her low-heeled, open toed shoes softened in the distance, she rhetorically exclaimed for all to hear, "I can tell you ain't gonna last too much longer around here."

HOLD UP AMERICA! That was a foul ball! Somebody blow the whistle. That nurse, sacheting by and giving sneak previews, is certainly not playing fair. I'm a GOD fearing Man, but why must thou tempt me.

No one understands the extent of my struggles!

I walked to the kitchen to get a cup of coffee, disappointed at myself, and then headed upstairs and waited for Ms. Johnson. In order for me to get to her office upstairs, I had to go through a series of check points. First the front desk calls up, then I check in upstairs, and then I have to wait for an escort into her office.

After waiting in a small room for 30 minutes, Ms. Johnson finally waddles off the elevator. Now I'm pissed, if she's going to fire me she could have saved me the trip!

I stood outside her door, next to the officer, uneasy and averse to crossing the threshold of her office. Watching, waiting and looking as if I were ready to jump Double-Dutch.

"Gimme a Ho if you got your funky bus fare. Ho!"

"Double-Dutch bus... Never mind"

Ms. Johnson was looking in her element doing her version of multitasking; talking on the phone to her daughter, playing Blackjack on her computer and listening to her favorite gospel CD. After kicking off her shoes that probably felt two sizes too small by 9:00 a.m., she turned in my direction and said in a surprisingly pleasant voice, "Have a seat Mr. King. I'll be with you in a minute."

The chairs in her office are wide and cushioned, unlike the concrete slabs I had grown accustomed to. The air is fresh, clean and filled with the smell of potpourri. Strangely her demeanor seemed to mesh and meld with the ambiance of the room. It was cordial, pleasant, uncharacteristically warm, and despite the fact that a guard is posted at the door like a sentry, it's intimate.

After hanging up the phone, she shifted her sights solely upon me and began performing her interview. Her eyes were brown, soft, warm, and full of concern. Her voice was husky yet gentle, stimulating yet soothing, nasal yet melodic. People have said that she acts tough but is really a big softy. Maybe they were right.

On her desk is a candy dish with assorted Cream Savers and a variety of miniature chocolate bars. Snickers, Nestle' Crunch, Almond Joy, Mounds, and even little bags of Sugar Babies.

I must have looked like a kid in a candy store waiting for the store clerk to turn his head so I could stuff my pockets, because she smiled and said, "Would you like some?"

I grabbed a Cream Saver and popped it in my mouth. The velvety smooth candy had a splash of fruit tanginess that tasted so good in my mouth that I began to check the wrapper to make sure it was Kosher.

"I've been watching you very closely Mr. King. I have to be honest with you; I don't think you're going to last around here too long." She paused for a second until our eyes met.

"Besides, all of our patients are already assigned volunteers, and since I don't need you coming over here doing nothing or getting into trouble, I'm unofficially assigning you a special case."

"What?"

And, as if we were not in the middle of conversation, she turned her back... and continued, "his name is Mr. Godsby."

I knew some bull-crap was in the mix because her conscience would not allow her to look at me as she said it.

"His name is Mr. Godsby. Okay...and?" I quizzed.

Unwilling, or unable, to continue with the charade, she turned and blurted out as if she were holding her breath, "AND-HE-IS-GETTING-ON-MY-DAMN-NERVES!"

The TRUTH must have set her free, because her smile returned, and she was able to face me again.

"He is buggin' me about every little thing that doesn't go his way. This is prison, not the Holiday Inn, I need you to teach him how to jail!"

23

Teach him how to jail? Does she think I'm soft or something? Does she think I've lost my fight? I'm Cinque the Mutineer, Nat Turner, Toussaint L'ouverture, Jamo Kenyatta the Burning Spear!

I grimaced from the thought and asked, "Teach him how to jail?"

"Mr. King, you know I'm a God fearing woman. I'm trying not to curse him out, but he rubs me the wrong way. I need you to school him. Take him under your wing, and as soon as another patient comes I'll personally reassign you."

I knew she had pulled out all stops when she flirted. Y'all women are so used to using your feminine wiles to get your way with men, that subconsciously you do it even in inappropriate circumstances.

"If you can get him to leave me alone for a month..." She looked up at the officer who was talking to a nurse in the hall and discontinued her statement.

She then reached her soft hand over the desk and shook my hand to close the deal and end our interview.

As I stood over her she scanned me from head to toe and said, "Oh, one more thing. Don't be getting too friendly with the nurses. No matter how much they flirt, if it comes between you and her job they'll cross you every time. And you'll end up in the hole with a beat down."

Mr. Godsby

24

When Mr. Godsby and I first met, I was apprehensive. Everyone had heard that he was being assigned a volunteer, and once they found out it was, me all sorts of people, some that I've never spoken to, were coming out the wood work to try and tell me how foul this dude is. But I know how these jailhouse rumors are. Some of these so-called gangsters and killers in here are worse than women when it comes to rumor.

When two men talk bad about another man while that other man is missing, a Real Man doesn't listen.

Mr. Godsby is a slim, pot bellied, hunch backed, cane walking, one-eyed, Quagmire looking, white guy that has worse luck than Schelp-Rock from the 'Flintstones.' However, despite the reigning opinions about him, he and I got along just fine.

We developed a routine where I would come in and we would find an empty table, play a card game called casino, talk, and drink coffee. He did most of the talking, but, I understood, I was his only friend.

Many of the other residents would come by and speak, and I began to establish relationships with them. Most would come to talk because I was a volunteer, so I could go to the kitchen and get coffee and snacks when it was available. Some of the dudes, though not yet terminal, were in rough shape.

Monday Morning Meetings

25

Every Monday morning Palliative Care volunteers are obligated to attend these meetings, contrived in theory, to be a form of therapy for burned out volunteers. It's a forum where we were afforded the opportunity to unload our pain by sharing with each other, learning from each others' experiences, and discussing issues that directly affect us as caregivers.

Building sentient ties and bonds of friendship with another human-being, only to watch helplessly as they wither and die can become spiritually sapping and emotionally exhausting.

For some, it further reinforces their unwillingness to experience any emotion outside of anger and rage, while others were reborn by experiencing sensations that they thought they no longer had.

The meetings are facilitated by Reverend Moyer, Deacon Pachelli, or Ms. Johnson. And, although there are some basic guidelines as to how a group should be run, each facilitator runs his or her group differently.

Palliative Care volunteers were originally selected, exclusively, from Reverend Moyers Deacon's Class. Because of the dynamics, the topic and discussion of the meetings tended to morph into an encore performance of Sunday's service. The spirits of the meetings were beautiful, and many of the members and staff looked forward to it every week.

Chaplain Moyer, who assiduously vied with South Woods administration to get Palliative Care off the ground, was somewhat protective of the program, and tended to run his groups strictly by text. Unfortunately, life rarely goes according to text. Prior to my becoming a volunteer, he and I had conversed on numerous occasions.

He's the head of Chaplaincy. So, whenever I was called to deliver the week's sermon, he would often sit in the back office and listen. Afterwards, he would call me to the side and comment on how well I spoke and on the contents of the message. Sometimes he would even suggest good topics to cover in the future. He was kind and courteous, but there was something in his eyes that appeared insincere. There was something in his voice that I just didn't trust. Every time this dude comes around my Spider Senses go crazy.

One week he ventured off his norm and shared with us about his childhood. As the circumstances affecting the core of his being unfurl, his face transformed and I saw someone else. Someone who wasn't being deceptive, manipulative, or controlling. His face bore the eyes of a child; eyes too young to be obscured by life's ills. An adolescent with abandonment issues. A young man who knows how it feels to be alone, in fear, and unable to trust. A kindred spirit.

Ms. Johnson's groups were less formal, and outright funny at times. A self-proclaimed Blackman

Basher; she can appear biased, opinionated, and domineering, but she is soft as drug store cotton.

Being locked up with a bunch of men for a few years, hundreds of miles away from family, with no visits, and 15 minute phone calls costing $17, my concepts and views in life progressively grew one sided; hardcore.

In her groups we might talk about anything! From World Politics to her late husband, I would be surprised at how open and honest she could be. Intimate interactions with the femininity of Ms. Johnson was both, healthy and humanizing for me, because it balanced my perspectives.

I particularly enjoyed Deacon Pachelli's groups. A devout Catholic, and licensed psychologist, who happened to be raised around the Mob, his points of view, to me, were refreshingly realistic, and by far the broadest. His humility, in the face of overt pot shots at his faith, was inspiring.

After attending Penn State for a few years, (I mean State Pen.), and being exposed to a few new books and ideas, I thought I knew something. With my newly discovered mental prowess, I turned into a verbal gunslinger, I lived for the opportunity to perform intellectual roughshod on all who dared to cross my path.

Decon Pachelli, though humble, had a swagger as well. One day I came into the group with the sword unsheathed, dying to misdirect some of the hurt and anger towards my ex-wife, who had left our sons with my

28

mother to run off with a woman. I guess she meant it when she had said before that she could never love another Man the way she loves me. Anyway, I had misdirected my indignation by ripping Ms. Johnson to shreds so deftly that she didn't even know it. That's when the Deacon intervened like Doc. Holiday in 'Tombstone,' when he told the rancorous Ringo, "I'll be your Huckleberry."

Of course, I accepted the challenge. He not only disarmed my bull-crap, but did so while tactfully slinging back some of his own, that was so smooth, most of the group didn't even smell it.

I was the overzealous student, foolishly challenging the Sensei, only to be defeated with a single blow. Deacon Pachelli, I thank you for stimulating my mind, humbling my character, and solidifying my sentiment of turning every person I come in contact with into my teacher.

By the Token of Time,

Throughout the Ages mankind has been at loss,

Except those who have faith, and do righteousness,

And enjoin each other in truth with patience and consistence.

Mr. White

Oct. 4 2004

Though I continue to spend time with Mr. Godsby, today I was assigned my first official patient and, I have to admit, I'm a little excited. They told me his name is Mr. White. We are encouraged to address each other with the title of Mister. That may seem like a small matter, but the titles that we address each other have an effect on our character.

Mr. White had been transferred from the infamous Trenton State Prison. After the Revolutionary War, a part of Trenton State was used as a horse stable. Remnants of posts and hooks are still embedded in stations where African Slaves were held. Trenton is so old and decrepit that in the mid 1800's Charles Dickens visited this place and condemned its conditions. Imagine what it is like 150 years later.

Mr. White suffered from chronic bronchitis, influenza, and severe arthritis. Though his body was wilted from age and disease, you could tell he was probably once a man of considerable size. His massive head donned high cheek bones and a prominent aquiline nose. His jaw line was strong, solid, and squared.

Now his heavily tattooed, translucent skin looms ghostlike. An anchor and the words U.S. NAVY were etched on his left forearm, and appears as if you could see right through the green ink.

The digits of his feet and hands would alternate, turning and twisting in diverging directions with wanton disregard of the joints with which they were attached; bruised and deeply discolored in shades of red, black, and green. They oddly reminded me of the Black National Flag.

In his mouth, one solitary tooth remained a whittled right incisor. It temerariously stood as a lone sentinel, bearing the standard of a plague ridden citadel. Elsewhere, his thin lips puckered inward in a vain attempt to close the gaping orifice.

I popped into the room, put my books on a table by the bed, and introduced myself. His condition was too far gone to respond. I found myself staring at his feet. The toes of which were pointing outward like a hitch hikers thumb. Since he was incoherent, I went and got myself some coffee, which usually turns into four or five trips for the other residents. By the time I got back to the room, his toes where pointing inwards! I'd never seen anything like that in my life; I'd never even heard of it.

Ms. Johnson came to the room.

"Good morning, Mr. King. I see you've met Mr. White."

"Yeah uh, I guess."

"The doctor is placing him on a Vigil and we are going to need you."

I'm gonna be honest with you, I'm not too keen of this whole Vigil business. Mind you, I empathize with the whole idea of not dying alone, but sitting bedside, after working whichever job the State requires you to work, and going to school, then sitting for six hours at a time. Six hours!

"We are putting you on for 12 to 6."

It didn't dawn on me, until she was gone, that she was talking about 12am. America, that's Graveyard Shift; I can't get Jiggy with that! I was trying to wiggle my way out of Graveyard shift, but nobody liked that shift, and I was too new to have the seniority to do so.

I caught Woody and Wicks, two group elders, in the volunteers break room and tried to cry my way out. Woody gave me a sympathetic eye. He's a good Christian brother, and is one of the nicest guys you ever want to meet: He reminds me of Ned Flanders from the Simpson's; "Heidi Ho!"

Wicks, the Black Frank Sinatra who has blue eyes and all, burst out laughing at my transparent attempts to get out of my new assignment. His laughter became contagious, and Woody and I got a chuckle or two.

Woody, in turn, began to relay one of his more memorable vigil experiences. He said the guy was the personification of a real 'Hells Angel'; a real tough guy biker dude, who fought death every step of the way. He fought, and fought, and fought death, until he had no more

33

fight left. Exhausted and semiconscious, he leaned up and stared directly into Woody's eyes. Woody said that he had noticed that the thick filmy white build up that had encased his retina had dissipated, as he fixed his gaze on a corner of the room right behind him. Naturally, Woody turned around to see who was behind him. But no one was there that he could see. The biker dude grimaced, and screamed, "Come on, I don't give a F*>K!" and died.

Wicks didn't help. He followed with his own rendition of his patient, who he had interacted with for almost a year. He was a big brawny man who looked as if he shouldn't have even been in the program. Slowly, his health began to fade and he began to lose weight. Eventually he had slipped into a coma. Even though he was comatose, Wicks would still come and talk to him, read books to him, and say prayers for him.

After a while, this became habit, and a part of Wicks' routine. He would come in, kick his shoes off, lean back while sipping on warm tea, and read his Daily Bread. (I'm Muslim, but like to read those too.)

One day, while Wicks was in his groove, his patient opened his eyes and leaned straight up. Wicks was elated to see his buddy back, and couldn't contain his smile; and Wicks doesn't smile often. He spoke to the man, but he paid Wicks no attention; he was too preoccupied with whatever it was in the corner. The same corner that Woody was talking about. In the same room. In the same room that Mr. White was in now!

The man, who had been in a coma for months, jumped up and attempted to run in the opposite direction. Whatever it was in that corner incapacitated him, and he died in mid-stride.

Needless-to-say I was slightly spooked, and I wasn't ready to go in that room, so I went outside to kick it with the fellas. Mr. Godsby was being cursed out by Mikey and Mr. Lopez and was kneeling over and rolling a cigarette.

"You know those things are bad for your health?"

"I gotta die from something." Then he stood up

Mr. Lopez's stomach was swollen like one of those starving Ethiopians they show on T.V. Mr. Lopez was an older Latino who had lived a rough life on the streets. He used all sorts of drugs and was a heavy drinker. He was dying from cirrhosis, and that was the reason that his stomach was swollen.

I would talk to him from time to time, but I knew better than to get religious. I had heard his response to one of the other volunteers who may have been pushing for him to get saved. It wasn't pretty.

Mikey was getting louder and began pointing his finger in Mr. Godsby's eye so I calmly put my hand on his shoulder and greeted him.

"As-Salamu alaykum"

"Wa...wa...wa salaykum as-salam"

"No Mikey. It's wa alaykum as-salam."

His huge eyes lit up like Christmas lights and he clapped his hands together, then began to jump up and down like a child. Then he smiled so hard that his mouth looked like an open box of yellow crayons.

Mikey was dying from A.I.D.S. His father was a musician in one of my all-time favorite groups and he too was a musician. Heavy drug use led to his demise.

Strung out on drugs, he and another guy had committed a robbery. When Mikey wasn't looking, his conspirator hit him in the back of the head with a blunt object, and left him to take the weight for the robbery. He woke up from a coma a year later. He had lost a great part of his memory and had to relearn how to walk and talk.

"Come on Mikey, leave that man alone." I said as I pulled him inside

"No-no-no ah-ah-akhi, he-he-he..."

"Stop it akhi, (Brother), we don't talk behind people's backs."

"Ah-ah-I'll tell him to his face!"

"Do me a favor, akhi; be nice."

"Okay"

Having done my good deed for the day, I was headed to Mr. White's room to get my books, and then back to the compound.

CODE 33

CODE 33

CODE 33

"Okay y'all, lock in!" Ms. Gould yelled.

I was accustomed to codes being called, so I knew that a code 33 meant that there was a fight in progress. To prevent potential riots, all parties that are not involved are locked in a secured area.

This is the first time I've been in one at E.C.U. The officer ordered me to lock in the room. The room that I've been avoiding all morning; the room with Mr. White.

The rooms over there were larger than those on the compound, and a long slender window was in the back. In the day-light hours, the rays of the sun provide enough ambient lumination to keep the rooms lofty and bright, but when I was forced to lock in the room with Mr. White, the room grew small, dark, cold, and constricting.

As I entered the door I was greeted with a blood curdling, spine tingling, Creature Feature, like a cry of sheer agony.

"OOOOooooOHHHH!"

"OOOOOooohhhhh!"

"OH-BOY, oh-boy!"

Just as the air we breathe has the ability to gently cool our skin on a sunny afternoon, or the unyielding power to uproot trees during a hurricane, you cannot see it, or taste it, or touch it, yet you know it's there. Metaphysical palpations to the rhythm of the unseen made the hairs on the back of my neck stand and do the 'Harlem Shake.' I was stuck in a realm that oddly felt familiar, yet like no place I have ever seen before. I felt as if the Grim Reaper was standing behind me with icy cool breath, awaiting the command to snatch my soul!

BOOM!

BANG!

BOOM!

Were the ear splitting acoustic affects of concrete and steel as Ms. Gould, with her fine self, slammed the door and shook the handle to make sure that it was locked.

I couldn't move. I couldn't breathe. I couldn't think! Ashton Kutcher may as well have jumped out of the closet, because I was straight PUNKED!

"OOOOOOOOOOooooohhhh" he howled, even louder than before.

"Okay Marte', breathe." I took a few deep breaths. Inhaling through my nostrils, consciously expanding my diaphragm, exhaling through my mouth and emptying my lungs in a slow and steady pace.

After regaining my composure, I asked Mr. White if he could hear me. He slowly looked at me for the first time and then looked away.

"Mr. White, can you hear me?"

He turned back in my direction and attempted to speak. He said, "Grrr...Grrr...grrrrrr," and ran out of breath.

"What?"

He lifted his arm and showed me his hospital identification bracelet. He's name is Thomas Grrr...

"Grrrrrr-Grrrreeee-grrreeeen!" he finished with a slight cough.

"Ma name is Thomas Green."

Winded, yet with a look of relief on his face, Mr. Green gazed upon me as if he had completed his life's mission. And died shortly afterwards.

I believe that everything has a purpose and that nothing happens by chance. The entirety of our conversation consisted of merely one sentence, yet its implications spoke volumes. This man, who I don't know from a can of paint, used his last breath to make sure that I knew his name before he died.

Mr. Green inspired me to strive with all that I have to make sure that you know my name.

You...

You've inspired me.

Dying, shriveled up, and decrepit, old Man.

You've inspired me.

I once sold drugs and robbed people to get things so that people would desire me.

Now I've come to realize that it is better for them to admire me.

Admire the Man that I AM!

Desired things are subject to weaken and fade, but admiration is the substance of which legends are made.

Marcus, Martin, Malcolm, Muhammad...

Marte'?

You've inspired me.

Nothing but change stays the same.

It was more difficult for me to find a place to study over here on Phase II. My Bunky (cell mate), though he is Muslim (and it's nice to have someone to pray with) is a young boy who did the River Dance on my last nerve! He's a Rapper who listens to Rap and Rock-n-Roll all day long! And in the day rooms it was either too loud, or I was bombarded by a thousand questions.

Fortunately, I found a place in the school area. Because the Communications course had some tapes with it and I didn't have a tape player, the Educational

Department allowed me to use the one they have in the school area.

The computer lab teacher, Mrs. Gould, was an older Puerto Rican lady who had gone back to school to get her Master's. She would go out of her way to help you if she believed that you were serious, but if she detected any foolishness she would jump on you with both feet! She served as a proxy when I took my mid-terms, and because of my study ethics we developed a rapport. She allowed me to use the computers to begin writing my first book, "One MannTeam."

Coming soon to a store near you!

The officer in charge of the school areas is named Boyd. He's a big man with an even bigger mind, who respects everyone. His knowledge on a wide range of topics amazed me. I would come in at anytime I was able to slide to his post and ask questions. I'd say, "Teach me something." He'd just smile and say "pick a topic." And although he is the police, and getting chummy with them is against 'Hardcore Prisoners' ethics, he became my mentor. I refused to allow peer pressure to deny me knowledge, and I have yet to pick a topic of which upon he wasn't able to tell me something that I don't know.

"Be ye changed by the renewing of your mind."

Romans 12; 1 & 2

Though the readjustment was difficult, I began to regain my equilibrium rather fast. Between teaching

41

classes in the chapel, going to the school area for tutelage, and going to E.C.U., my schedule was packed. Just the way I like it!

Although I didn't have to, I continued to give Mr. Godsby quality time. He could get on your nerves, but he was a fighter; a man after my own heart. After hanging out with Godsby for over 6 months, I realized that he was beyond cynical; he was out right paranoid. The crazy part is that, by some unexplainable force, I believe he was bringing misfortune into Fruition by his thoughts. Then the misfortunes substantiated and perpetuated his paranoia.

"Thoughts in our minds have made us. What we are by thought is fashioned and built. If a man has evil thoughts, pain comes to him... If one endures in purity of thought, joy follows him as his own shadow."

Napoleon Hill

He confided in me what had happened to his eye. He said that rumor had gone around that he was a 'Snitch;' and somebody slipped into his cell and beat him mercilessly with his own cane. He showed me the pictures that the investigators took of his room afterwards; blood was everywhere!

It looked like the guy had knocked his eyeball smooth out his head, and that's what I had thought, until he opened his eyelid, and showed me that it was actually beaten as flat as a pancake.

It gets worse! He was labeled a 'Snitch' in part, because when he was at Rahway (the prison where Sylvester Stallone's movie, "Lock Down", was filmed) he had had a bunky with mental health issues, and they got into an argument. Because he had gotten into a bad motorcycle accident his spine is fused and his mobility limited. So was his fight game. He said his bunky, a much bigger man, punched him in the face, bent him over, and raped him. He said he was screaming, swinging his arms, and kicking but he couldn't stop him. He tied him up and raped him several times for three days straight. His bunky was H.I.V. positive.

America, I have to be honest with you; when he first told me he was raped, repeatedly, in 2004, I couldn't help but think that he must have wanted it. That type of stuff just doesn't happen any more... I guess it does. Still, as bad as it may sound, I could no longer stand the sight of him. I just looked over at old man, Sal, as he smoked his hand-rolled cigarette. It was as if he had told me he was a pedophile, and it was simply too hard for me to mask my discomfort. I played it off by telling him I needed to go back early, but I know that he felt my vibe.

Strangely, on my trek back to the compound, it was if time had stopped. The weather was warm, there was no breeze, and it was slightly humid. No one was on the grounds. No officers. No prisoners. No staff. Just me and my conscience, which weighed wearily on my back, like a concrete sweat suit in quicksand, and that walk was the

43

longest walk ever. That man broke down and confided tragic occurrences in his life because he trusted me. He's a victim yet; my street-bred lack of respect for those who allow themselves, in my opinion, to be victimized, unconsciously manifested and made me sick to the stomach. I realized the person that I am, at times, is still in conflict with the Man that I am striving to become.

"Have mercy upon me, O GOD, according to Your loving-kindness; according to the multitude of Your tender Mercies, blot out my transgression. Against You, You only, have I sinned, and done this evil in Your sight..."

Psalms 51

April 2005

Around this time a constant procession of setbacks, disappointments and heartaches, numbed my ability to feel, and left me somewhat anesthetized to the sufferings of Man.

I had just received notice that my appeal for a sentence reduction had been denied, and all the mishaps that occurred during my trial had effectively been swept under the rug of legal jargon. I gotta put up with daily abuse from an officer who had just came back from Iraq and stares at me like he wishes this was Abu Ghraib. I have a manipulative Muslim rallying a coup against my leadership. A leadership that I never wanted! All because he has the audacity to request that I disallow these young brothers getting caught up in these gangs from coming to Islamic services, when he's the self proclaimed King of a known Muslim gang! And, on the other hand, tension amongst the prison population is at an all time high, behind these young boys, many of whom are getting down for protection, joining these gangs, and now all a sudden, they're tough. Every day somebody is getting beat down, jumped in, or given "Buck Fifty's". A "Buck Fifty" is a cut across the face, so severe that you need 150 stitches to close the wound. To top all of that off, my ex-wife, who claims to be waiting, because she can never love another man the way she loves me, moved to Arizona to live with my mother. She ended up running off, and leaving the kids with my mom for a lesbian affair! When it rains, it pours.

Drowning in a dirty toilet of wasted hopes and aspirations, with no one to blame but myself, I felt as if this place was slowly suffocating the essence of my soul. However, I kept going, I kept striving, and I keep looking for the next lesson.

Each person handles the pangs of impending death differently. Some get angry, and complain about each and everything imaginable; cussing and fussing at everyone within earshot; while others introspect, or become religious to remain steadfast. I don't know if it's psychological or not, but the latter are the ones who have a more peaceful passing.

I've watched quite a few men go through their transition towards the "Inevitable," but none more chronic and grueling than those suffering from liver complications. Mr. Lopez, the guy who cursed out the Christian Brother for trying to preach the Word to him had Cirrhosis of the liver and died the most horrible death imaginable. His body had become so emaciated that he was merely skin and bones. His body literally decomposed while he was perfectly conscious. That's worse than being buried alive! And had I not seen this with my own eyes, I may not have believed it.

He already had to go to an outside hospital to get his stomach pumped to remove all of the toxic fluid build-up, that had caused his abdomen to swell larger than a fat lady having twins. After a while, they inserted a plug into his side, to be drained every few days, like letting air out of a bag of some jailhouse hooch. *Perfect commercial:*

THIS, IS YOUR BODY ON ALCOHOL

And remember kids, Intoxication means to poison yourself!

*It was so bad that the doctor had to come to his room every few days to scrape his tongue because fungus was growing in his mouth like a Chia Pet! And though Mr. Lopez was staunchly anti-religious at first, by the time he had died, he'd become a Born Again Christian, a Catholic, and a Muslim. Messed me up when one day I walked into the room and he said, "Salaam alaykum!" We all just prayed for him to die. **True Story.***

Conversely, every person I met with some sort of faith died so smoothly, even in suffering, that it strengthened my faith. One example of this, for me, was a brother name Alamin.

He's one of the few guys I knew prior to him coming to E.C.U. When he told me that he had cancer and had been going to chemo for over a year, I was amazed because he never lost his beard. I guess that's why nobody ever knew he was sick. Alamin was a serious brother, most of the time, who was very knowledgeable but also a comedian.

He stood up and began walking in place like a soldier and explained what had prompted him to come to the hospital. He said that the cancer began to advance and

47

it had reached his spinal cord. All the while he was still walking in place.

"I was walking down the compound and I kept smelling something foul. A movement to the gym was in progress so I had to stop and wait for a minute until 5 house went inside." Then he stopped walking

"I felt something roll down my leg." giving off an expression of surprise as he looked on the ground to reenact the account.

"I couldn't feel my grippers."

"Your what?" I asked.

"My gripper's akhi!" he repeated as he hit himself on the butt.

"That was a turd that rolled down my leg!"

I tried to hold back my laughter but the way he said it, I was in stitches!

"Man, I was so embarrassed; I started looking all around like I didn't know where that turd came from."

By this time I was on the floor crying! I hadn't laughed so hard in months.

After our laughter, his face emerged, more seriously; he commended me for my services and gave me words of inspiration. It was just what I needed to remove the funk that I was in. I gave him a hug, in parting, and promised to come visit him the next day. He died that evening, peacefully, in his sleep.

Every morning I'd see this peculiar guy, known to everyone, as the Colonel. He would be posted up in front of one of the dayrooms that are located in front of the officer's desk.

He would look in my direction, sometimes, as I came through but I wasn't sure if the medication cocktail that he was on enabled him to focus beyond the cup of coffee he was trying to drink. Half of which was all over his wrinkled up shirt and pants.

Colonel had the look of a Madman in his eyes and when he talked, he sounded like Bobcat Goldwaithe needing Lithium. His finger tips were literally burned to a crisp, from smoking hand rolled cigarettes down to the fire.

Omar, the barber in E.C.U., had told me about Colonel a while ago. He said that Colonel is crazy as a nut in a fruit house and notorious for attacking people for no apparent reason. Bar none! He'll throw hot piss on a C.O. as well. Hot piss! He may be crazy, but if he ever threw one of those chumpies on the Kid... Well, you know!

Anyway, after a few months of my volunteering I began to notice that whenever it was time for me to leave, he would be in the same spot, waiting. Except now he would stare at me in a creepy way.

49

"What's up Colonel?" I asked, apprehensive, yet my normal congenial self.

"Goth ah anvalupe?"

"What?"

He raised his voice as if this would increase my ability to interpret his native tongue.

"Yew gotha anvalupe?" and looked at me like I was stupid.

"Oh! No Colonel, I don't have an envelope."

"Oak-a Blah-blah-blah, Ba-blah-blah-blah."

I think he said okay, but that's all I could understand of that. I nodded my head like I understood, and made a Beeline for Mr. Goh's room.

Mr. Goh

Subject to the patterns of addiction; hopes and dreams aren't the only thing caught in its whirlwind of destruction. Spirits, minds, and bodies are significantly, and sometimes irrevocably, damaged. Hopelessness, depression, and HIV/AIDS are only a few of its maladies.

Mr. Goh had Hepatitis and Cirrhosis. As long as I've been assigned to him, I've never heard him say a word, or even acknowledge my presence. In a way, it seemed that he was being rude, but if I was in as much pain as he obviously was, I probably wouldn't be too pleasant to be around, either.

My job is to be of service, and this entails doing my best to be helpful, respectful, and kind regardless of the patients' disposition. Sometimes I talk. Sometimes I clean up their rooms or bring whatever snacks are available. Sometimes I'm silent, but I'm there, and often that's all they need to feel more at ease.

He, like majority of the men who I have watched die in this program, had no outside visitors. It's a shame to be on your death bed and have no mother, sisters, brothers, children, cousins, wives, or girlfriends coming to see you on your last days. There are civilian volunteers that take time out of their lives to come in and comfort these unfortunates. May GOD bless them with the greatest of blessings.

One day, after finishing an extremely good cup of 'Hype' (Coffee) I walked in Mr. Goh's room to pay him a visit. The caffeine had me running off at the gibbers like I had diarrhea of the mouth, when Mr. Goh turned towards me and said something inaudible.

This marked the first time he had ever said something to me. This was huge, vast, colossal, and stupendous!

Did I mention that I had just drunk some 'Hype'?

"Mr. Goh, did you say something?" I eagerly quizzed.

"Yeh moo-da-fook-ka, shoot-da-fook-cup!" looking dead in my eyes.

"What!" I ask rhetorically. "I know you didn't just..."

As if to answer my question, he turned around and faced the fly trap hanging over his bed, in the opposite direction.

Aw Hell naw! I know this little no good, burnt-faced, rat-mouth, rotten rainbow colored toothed, glow in-the-dark, Ming the Merciless, fake-ass mix between Kayto and the Green Hornet looking joker didn't just call me a Mother...mother...

All I could think about was, what would Tyler Perry's 'Madea' do right now? Hmm

And since I can't do that, I'm going to leave before I give him a piece of my mind.

Peace be still...

Before I pick up a piece of steel.

As I walked out of the room to get my I.D. off of the front desk and go, the two regular officers, along with Ms. Johnson, were sitting behind the desk with overtly dirty looks on their faces. They looked at me like they wished me harm. They snarled at me like they hated my guts. Three African American women, all of whom are beautiful in their own way, gritted on me like I stole their momma's pocket books.

I'm not conceited, but I've been accustomed to being looked upon with veneration, to some degree, since I was a child. Remarks like, 'Oh he's a cute little baby," and as I got older, "He's a handsome young man," to "Girl, he is fine!" So, to get outright dirty looks, from women, is extremely discomforting. And I began to get paranoid.

I hated that feeling! And it caused me to question myself and my approach towards dealing with these people. I'm an African American Muslim, convicted felon, with considerable size, and looks that can be mistaken as mean. I realize that. I realize that I can intimidate others with my looks. I have done so, with ease, for years. I also knew that it was dangerous to have people be afraid of you. So I do my best to contain my natural inclinations of dominance. But sometimes, in trying to appear less *threatening, I feel like I'm being played for a chump. I'm gonna have to resolve this issue, tactfully, and soon, before the person I am overpowers the Man I am striving to become.*

Medication is being dispensed at the desk. And the medication line is like the government cheese line; that joint reaches clear around the corner. Most of the guys housed here are in pretty rough shape, and it would not be strange to see a brother roll up in a wheelchair with a portable I.V. hanging out of his arm.

There was one guy in particular who made me grateful for my good health. He suffered from frequent and debilitating seizures. A tall, handsome, athletically built guy with brilliant blue eyes that looked like they had sparks of energy crystals glitter around his retina.

He's one of those proud types of dudes, who don't like for people to show sympathy towards him or give special treatment; he just wanted to be treated like everyone else. I would do just that.

Fearing he would fall out and tear the stitches that were already in his head, the doctors ordered him to wear a helmet. You know he was not feelin' that!

Now mind you, he doesn't like special treatment, so as soon as I saw him I treated him like anybody else; I started to Jone (crack jokes) on him. And I could tell he appreciated it. When I called him a broke down Crash Dummy, he burst into laughter so hard I thought he was about to have another seizure! It may have been because of his broken teeth but this is the first time I had seen him laugh. Till this day they call him Crash.

Just as the menacing stares of the Queens of E.C.U. shrank me, the looks I received from this motley crew of patient's faces strengthened my fortitude and heightened my convictions. And I'm reminded of why I'm over here in the first place. If that means warding off the angry stares and harsh sentiments of three black women, so be it. But if Ms. Gould weren't so dag-on gorgeous, and Ms. Evans's lips weren't so... never mind.

I walk back in the room and hit Mr. Goh with my customary hello. He didn't even turn to acknowledge my presence.

"I'm just stopping by to see if there is anything I can do for you." I said in my cheeriest voice.

His eyes were fixed on a fly perched on the ceiling above his bed. There was no reply. He didn't even look at me, but that was cool. I had already decided to be there for him regardless, so I sat down and pulled out my journal.

Dear Journal:

I've been with Mr. Goh for about a week now, and I still don't even know his first name. He just lays there in a pair of cut off long johns that are extra yellow and brownish around the armpits and in the crotch areas. At one point in his life, he'd been severely burned, I don't know for sure, but I'd say at least 80% of his body. His arms, neck, torso, legs, and even feet were covered with the waffle-like marks of skin-graphs. His face appeared to have been untouched by the flames, yet the scars of enduring unspeakable afflictions wrap around his head like the turban of a Bedouin Arab. His eyes were greenish yellow and his facial features looked akin to the stereotypical bad guy in the old Karate' movies.

I wonder what happened to his body. Those don't look like ordinary burns. I wonder if he had been a political prisoner who was tortured. Or maybe a Yakuza caught in a room where a Molotov cocktail had been thrown? Putting down my pen, I let my imagination run wild.

'Deep in the jungles of Southeast Asia I stand. The air is humid and the soil is soft, pungent, and moist; perfect for booby traps and trip lines. The smell of gun powder residue splashes my face as I raise my fully loaded M-16 cautiously. In a place like this, you can never be too careful. The sight of something moving through the thick foliage instantly shoots adrenaline through my system, quickening my pulse. I feel sorry for whoever pops up unannounced, friend or foe; I'm going to unload every one of these full metal jackets in his....

"Mr. King!"

"Mr. King!"

"Mr. King!"

"Boy, what's wrong with you?" Ms. Johnson asked as she stomped her fat little feet to get my attention.

"Na..nothing-nothing, I-I-I was just thinking about something."

Extending her corpulent 14k gold and diamond clad French manicured fingers as if she was palming a basketball, she said, "With that big head of yours, you better not be thinking too hard, you might hurt something."

"Oh, you wanna Jone on my head? What you really need to do is stop being cheap and treat yourself to a real manicure, because if one of them press-on nails pop off, I'm gonna ride you for a week!"

She mumbled under her breath, just loud enough for me to hear, "You couldn't last five minutes."

I heard her, but I still asked, "What you say?" struggling not to smile.

With a slight smile, she put her hands on her hips and turned with an attitude and said, "You would never get the chance to ride me... with your big head self."

"I told you I don't play the head jokes." I returned, and then sheepishly lowered my head, "I'm sensitive."

She stomped her feet, and rolled her neck, in unison, while saying, "I'll talk about whatever I want to talk about." Then she leaned close enough for me to feel the warmth of her breath as she whispered, "You got a problem with that?"

DANGER, DANGER, DANGER Will Robinson!

I had to slide my chair back, and lower my blood pressure, yet my sights had difficulty making it all the way up to her face.

"Don't open doors that you really can't handle being open. Because you'll be going to the police if I say something about those big ole..."

She jumped back and folded her arms across her belly and said, "My big ole what?"

Uh-oh, here comes the bullcrap.

"I know I'm fat. I've been fat all my life. It don't bother me, and ain't nothing you can say that I ain't heard before. Go ahead, say it! What you scared?"

Whoa! Where did that come from? I better make my next move, my best move.

"Girl, you just trippin' cause you got on a new dress. Walking in here like you Tina Turner of sumpthin', and showing off them pretty toes."

She started smiling from ear to ear. So I leaned a little closer.

"You know I got a thing for pretty toes."

"Boy, you crazy."

"I keep telling you that I ain't no Boy." I stood up so she could feel my frame tower over hers.

"Okay Mr. King, I can respect that."

"I may be a lowly peasant in your eyes but that is all I ask for."

"You may think that my life has been a bowl of cherries compared to yours, but it hasn't."

I could see the pain in her eyes as she recalled her not so distant past.

"For years my ex-husband abused me; mentally and physically. He made me believe that I was unworthy of love, and that no one would want me, but him. He made me feel stupid and undesirable, and I accepted it. I believed it." She turned and looked at herself through a stainless steel plate, that's a makeshift mirror, posted above the sink. After brushing herself off, she asked, "Tell me, Mr. King, why do you think I accepted it?"

I might be crazy, but I would be a fool to answer that one.

"I'll tell you. I accepted it because, for years, I didn't love myself. After he died, my life truly began. I got back into the Word, and went back to college."

We made eye contact, I nodded my head in affirmation and she continued.

"Now that I have GOD in my life, I don't need no man to make me feel whole or worthy of love. I don't need no man at all."

I gave her the, 'yeah right' look, and removed a paper from my briefcase.

"All I need is Jesus!" twirling around like Miss Piggy in a Tutu. "Look at me now. I got a job that pays good money and..."

"How much money you make?" I interrupted while smartening a falsetto mustachio.

She shot me a look that said, 'Ne-gro Please" and continued where I cut her off. "..and I teach bible classes at the college. I love myself today, and I-got-it-going-on!" Smiling as if she had just realized it.

"Stop frontin', Ms. Johnson, I saw that same story on Dr. Phil."

After smacking me upside the back of my head she yelled, "See, that's why I can't stand you." And as much as she tried not to, she fell out laughing.

"I must remind you of your ex-husband?"

"Why you say that?"

"Because every time you talk to me in front of people, you go out of your way to make it seem like you dislike me."

"No-I-don't," she said with a slight smile."

"Yes you do."

To give me enough time to put my erupting emotions back in check, I had to walk over to Mr. Goh and pretended to adjust something on his bed.

"I can only imagine the lies, tricks, and games that were played on you by him, but you can't blame me for something somebody else has done."

"I-I..."

"My hands don't call for it!" she could hear the seriousness in my voice.

"But..."

"Do you realize how difficult you have made my life over here?"

"I...but...Boy-Mr. King, what are you talking about?"

"This is South Woods! You are the Social Worker in lock-up; you know how these officers get down!"

She looked up at me for a second and then put her head back down.

"If a prisoner has beef with one officer, he's got beef with all; especially the female officers!"

"I'm not a.."

"Ms. Evans is respected and has time in the system. Ms. Gould is the prettiest officer in South Woods! All kinds of officers are over here sniffing up under her, and you know it. All they have to do is act like they have a problem with me and I'm not safe anywhere in the prison. These women are your girlfriends. If you act like you can't stand my guts, they are gonna follow suit!"

Her eyes widened as if she had an epiphany.

"You know I'm telling the truth. I've been volunteering, everyday, faithfully, for the last 6 months. Whether in rain, snow, or blazing heat, I'm here. On my free time, for free, I'm here. I have other things that I could be doing. I have other responsibilities. I'm not asking for special treatment, from you or anybody else, I just want to be treated as a Man!"

Tears began to well up in my eyes as the pain and hurt of the past months struggled to the surface.

In a voice filled with compassion and empathy, she slowly began to explain, "Mr. King, believe it or not, I don't view you like my ex-husband and I don't dislike you."

Then she smiled as if she wanted to say something else.

"What I dislike is to see brothers like you in prison; handsome, young, strong, and intelligent black males playing games with your lives."

"I feel you on that Ms. Johnson. That's why I'm striving, daily, to make myself a better father, son, and Man."

"That's a good start, but that don't make you no Man."

"What?!"

"You heard what I said!" refusing to recognize the swelling of my chest.

"Tell me, who's taking care of your children?"

"Who's paying for those collect phone calls, which are so high that you need a part time job just to pay for them? Who's catching buses in the rain, with children, and standing in lines for hours, just to see you? Who? WE are! That's who. The women you guys leave behind to fend for ourselves."

Sweating, and on the verge of hyper ventilations, I could see the affects of the pain and suffering inflicted on thousands of beautiful women (mothers, sisters, wives, girlfriends, and daughters) in her eyes.

That was deep!

"How is Mr. D. Jesus?" she said, changing the subject.

"His name is DeJesus, D-Hey-Zeus; breaking down each syllable.

"Whatever."

"Whatever? What college did you say you graduated from?" I sarcastically gibed.

"It wasn't Jail-Bird U." she said as she poked me in the chest.

"Touché', it's about time you said something funny. Mr. D. Jesus seemed good the last time I saw him." I returned with a smile.

"Good, 'cause his family is coming to visit this afternoon. If his room needs cleaning up..."

WHAP! That was the sound made from her smacking me in the back of my freshly shaved head. Then she continued, "...handle that!" and bopped out the room like a teenager.

Before heading off to Mr. Dejesus' room, I straightened up a little for Mr. Goh, grabbed my briefcase, and was out. Mr. Goh almost caught a jab-left-right-uppercut when he rose up in his bed like the Crypt Keeper, frightening the crap out of me! His eyes were wide, and it looked like a puppy when his owner just comes home from school.

"AAAAAAAHHHHH, Moo-da-fook-ka!" he said, like it was a term of endearment.

His lips were so dry and crusty that I'm surprised he could smile. Without asking, I tore up a package of lemon swabs and gingerly moistened his ruptured lips. I had to be extra careful not to entangle a piece of skin in the fabric. That would be like pulling a hang nail on your lips. Ouch!

Since I was on a roll, I opened a pink lolly-pop looking, bubble-gum flavored, sponge tipped toothbrush. After dipping it in water, I began brushing his teeth.

He hasn't eaten or drank anything in three days. And his tongue has deep fissures and cracks that look like a mix between the hot barren sands of the Serengeti and a bad case of Athlete's Foot. I'm not sure if his tongue looks like that because of the lack of water, or if he hasn't eaten because he could not bear the pain of putting something in his mouth.

I wondered if he would get as bad Mr. Lopez. I wouldn't wish that on my worst enemy.

"Mr. Goh, you want some ice?"

He nodded yes, another first. I figured his teeth would be kind of sensitive, so I broke out the patented, handy dandy, "Ghetto Blender 2000." First, take a handful of ice cubes and stuff them inside of an un-powdered latex glove and hold the ends to secure the opening. Then, liberally bang the bag against any hard surface until the cubes break into small pieces, and you're ready to serve.

As soon as he saw the ice, he turned into one of those suburbanite little kids, whose parents don't believe in beating children, that you see in the supermarkets, driving their mother's crazy (You know the ones.); motioning frantically for me to give him some ice immediately when five minutes ago, he wasn't even thinking about ice. Since he wanted to rush me, I popped a whole cube in his mouth, just to be funny. He started *crunching on that ice cube like it was a Red Delicious apple!*

"Hold up man, slow down a little. You almost bit my finger."

I don't know if he understood me, but we had officially broken the proverbial ice.

He motioned for another piece.

"Okay, but if you bite my finger, I don't care how sick you are, or what kind of kung fu you know, I'ma kicking dat green ass!"

He looked up, smiled a little, and kept on crunching.

For the next three or four days I would come in, wash his face, brush his teeth, use a lemon swab and A & D ointment on his crusty lips, and then give him ice. It seemed like he was getting better. I knew from previous experiences that a patient will often get a burst of life right before he dies, so I didn't get too optimistic.

Dawn, one of the nurse's aides, asked me to help her put Mr. Goh in the shower. Many of the volunteers have no problem with changing soiled Man diapers, removing the urine and feces by wiping private parts, and showering their patients. I'm not one of those, but I commend those that do.

"Hold up Shorty, I ain't wit dat washing up no dudes' private parts and all" I quickly added.

She laughed and said, "I'm not asking you to. I just need you to help me put him in the shower." Then she scanned me slowly, from head to toe. Allowing her gaze to linger in certain areas and continued, "I can handle ALL of that!"

Did she just...never mind.

On that note, I walked down to Mr. Dejesus' room. Mr. Dejesus had just come from Trenton State, and suffers from prostate cancer. I don't know why, but for some reason his lower extremities were swollen up like a woman pregnant with twins. It was so bad he had to sleep in a reclining chair. Although he was in obvious pain, his demeanor was pleasant and content.

Every chance I got, I popped my head in the room to see if there was anything I can do to help. Usually he'd say no, but sometimes he'd begin to explain how his family is pushing for him to get a medical pardon.

I didn't mention it, but I've seen people in worse condition than him get denied medical pardons. In fact, in the history of the Palliative Care program, no man has ever obtained a medical pardon, even though our patients are diagnosed to have six months or less to live.

I wished him well and picked up a few pieces of refuse and headed to the trash.

By the time I made it to one of the big green garbage cans parked in front of the dayroom, Dawn flagged me down to help her bring Mr. Goh back to his room.

"Goth a anvalope?" Colonel asked, standing in front of Mr. Goh's room.

"No brother, I'll bring you one tomorrow."

"Oak a." Colonel laughed and went about his business.

If there is one thing I can say about Dawn, she really cares about her patients. So when she began to lotion Mr. Goh up, I left the room to give him some privacy.

Plus this was a perfect time to get a cup of 'Hype,' so I went down to the kitchen and grabbed up a few perks. On the way back, 'Hype' in one hand, buttered toast and yogurt in the other, Ms. Evans called me to her desk.

Ms. Evans had big, sexy lips that she drenched in candy apple red lip gloss. I never looked in her face because, no matter how hard I tried, whenever she spoke to me, I found it difficult not to lust.

"King, come here for a minute." the tone of her voice sounded solemn.

"What's up?"

"King, I know you think I'm hard on you, but I need for you to know that regardless of what it may seem,

68

I respect you. *According to our guidelines, we are not to get friendly or familiar with you guys. I'm a woman working in a prison full of men. I've been around a long time and I've seen a lot of things. Some of you guys are real smooth, if you know what I mean. Coming over here to get one of the nurses, or officers, that is stupid enough to fall for you."*

"Me?"

"I don't necessarily mean you. Listen, everybody knows this place is called the 'Love Shack.' You and I both know the deal; and so does the administration. Every now and then, an inmate that they really don't want over here slides through the cracks. When that happens, the Lieutenant will come down and look at the roster of names, and put a little mark by it. Your name has a big mark! Now do you understand? I'm just doing my job. But no matter how tough I am, I still respect you as a man. I mean that."

I nodded my head and was able to look at her face without staring at her lips.

YES! I was beginning to think that I'd lost my Mojo.

When I got to Mr. Goh's room he was all dressed. She must have caught a whiff of his breath when he was in the shower, WHOA!, 'cause she had goo gobs of toothpaste on a brand new toothbrush. I tried to stop her, but it was too late.

"UUUUHHHH! UUHHHHH! UH!" he screamed with his arms and feet kicking and flaying in place like Fred Flintstone starting up his car.

It was hilarious! Mr. Goh's eyes opened wide like he just took a mega-dose of Crystal Meth, his mouth was foaming like a rabid dog, and he was trying with all his might to stand up and fight, but the floor was too slippery.

I ran over and put him in a bear hug before he either knocked Dawn out or busted his head on the floor. Gently allowing my body weight to ease him back in the chair, I explained to her that I usually use the swabs for his mouth, while he continued kicking and screaming. I guess after the sting wore off, he realized who was holding him, he looked in my face with a sigh of relief, and said, "AAAAh, Moo-da-fook-ka," And we all fell out laughing.

Mr. Goh died later that day.

In the book THINK & GROW RICH by Napoleon Hill, the author cites: One of the most common causes of failure is the habit of quitting when one is overtaken by temporary defeat. In it, he relays a story about a gold miner who gives up when he was only three feet away from a fortune!

My gold mine, and sole purpose for volunteering, is to do some good deeds; to be of service, to give my time

70

and efforts freely, for once in my life, in hopes of becoming a better person.

If I had allowed the dirty looks Ms. Johnson and crew, or ill treatment of Mr. Goh, to deter me, then I would have went out like a sucker, and abandoned my treasure.

Men like Mahatma Gandhi and Dr. Martin Luther King left a legacy of lessons for mankind to follow. These men were not merely religious leaders and Civil Rights activists. These men were Masters in the art of patiently persevering.

By the Token of Time

Throughout the Ages,

Mankind has been lost.

Except those who have faith, and do righteous deeds,

And enjoin each other in Truth,

With patience and consistency.

The Colonel

September 9, 1940 to May 2, 2005

Colonel was one of those guys that stuck out like a sore thumb. Five foot ten, bald, toothless, and talked as if he were missing half of his tongue. When he got a fresh shave, he looked like that old man dancing on the Six Flags commercials.

Except for a brief halfway house stay in 1991, Colonel had been locked up since 1966. People who knew him said he used to be a Reverend and he would passionately preach what he believed to be the Words of God.

He was also a paralegal who worked feverishly to help others, often times for free! Now most paralegals will only put forth a satisfactory effort, if you're paying cartons of Newports; and act, in most cases, no differently than Public Defenders. (Whatever happened to the passion of bringing forth justice? Maybe it is Just-us.) He was so adept in his craft that his research was instrumental in getting a Death penalty case overturned.

In the 1990's, Colonel began to suffer from the affects of Alzheimer's disease. In April of 1997, Colonel was given the dubious title of the very first patient admitted into South Woods E.C.U. Although he suffered from a mental illness, he still managed to command a level of respect that few enjoyed.

72

Colonel drank coffee and smoked hand rolled cigarettes non-stop! He would often smoke them down so low that you could hear his flesh sizzling from the flame. His finger tips were literally burnt to a crisp. It was horrible. Sometimes they would even bleed.

When he didn't smoke the cigarette down to the skin he would stuff them in his sock, while they were still smoldering! As a result, his legs and ankle were burnt. I guess that he was impervious to pain. I tried to stop him a couple of times, but he wasn't trying to hear that. Plus, I had to be cautious; he was known for sucker-punching people for less.

Don't let the looks fool you, as old as he is, Colonel will fight anybody, in a heartbeat! He's thrown hot piss on Officers. They probably would have killed him if he were not on 'Special Needs.'

'Special Needs' patients are those inmates who are suffering from mental illness. Millions of dollars have been usurped from 'true' mental health facilities and transferred to prisons.

These prisoners bring in more money per bed space than a normal convicted felon. Subsequently, they are assigned advocates who more closely monitor their status. By policy/law, a 'Special Needs' prisoner must be evaluated within 24 hours after going to the hole.

The beatings that are customarily administered to prisoners going to the hole take longer than 24 hours to heal. So, these advocates grant a protection to 'Special Needs' prisoners that are not afforded to prisoners who are deemed sane.

Omar the barber and Colonel were pretty tight. As soon as Colonel sees Omar, the first thing he says is, "Wanna Fight?' and throws up is dukes. Omar would play fight with him for a minute and they would end up hugging each other. Colonel loved it! I tried to play fight with him once and he looked at me like I was crazy. Can you imagine how it feels to be looked at like you're crazy by someone who really is?

After about 8 months of seeing me every day, Colonel finally said more to me than "Gemme a 'moke" or "Gemme um cawfee." It took two months for me to figure out he was asking me to give him a smoke or some coffee.

"I like you, you are a good person," Colonel said in a raspy yet amazingly clear voice. Then he began to giggle, and continued with, "You're handsome and you have nice eyes. You can tell a lot about a person from his eyes," and burst into hysterical laughter.

I couldn't help but wonder if this dude was flirting with me.

"U goth anvalupe?" Colonel asked.

"Not on me, I'll bring you one when I come in tomorrow." I returned, wondering if he could actually write a letter.

"Oak a" he said as he turned and walked away, forgetting to ask for coffee.

When I came in the next day with his envelope, he just grabbed it and walked away. He didn't ask for coffee again. I wondered what was wrong with him.

Later that day, he called me from across the officers' desk, "Hey, Handsome!"

The officers turned in my direction trying to figure out who the Colonel was referring to. I was beginning to feel really uncomfortable with a man, no matter how crazy, calling me handsome. Gazing at me with a toothless grin, I eased towards Colonel, hoping no one realized he was talking to me. When I get there he handed me a makeshift check made out of the blank envelope I had given him earlier. The top of the check read, Bank of Edison. It was made out for one million dollars. Then he said, "This is so you can finish going to school."

How did he know that I had run out of college funding?

Every day, for a month, he wrote a check for me. I took it as a message from GOD to keep on striving, even though things look impossible. I felt good, at peace, and not so alone. It was exactly what I needed for that time.

After already receiving 100 million gazillion fafillion dollars, Colonel called me. I knew he wanted to write me another check.

"Want me to draw you a picture?" he asked with a toothless grin

"Sure" I returned, temporarily distracted by the greetings of a chocolate brown nurse who called herself Charlie.

He drew a picture of a cartoon mouse that had another mouse riding on its back. The riding mouse wore a striped top hat. They both had captions coming out of their mouths. The big one said "I'm a mouse, I like cheese." The little one said "Me, too!"

I cracked up. This went on for at least two months. Every now and again, he would change the captions, but everything else was the same. I had collected so many pictures from Colonel that I began giving them to people. Most of them got just a big as kick out of the pictures as I did. I even sent a few to my mother.

One day, in early July, I watched as Colonel went about his morning ritual; "cawfee" and "ah 'moke". When he returned from outside he was dizzy and barely able to walk. They took him to the hospital. When he returned, we learned that he had lung cancer. He died shortly thereafter.

When Colonel died, it was amazing to see how many people who were affected by his strange persona. Officers and prisoners mourned; some even cried.

At first I looked at those million dollar checks as worthless gestures of a man who had lost his mental *faculties. Then I remembered the smile that it put on my face. My lesson from Colonel is: no matter what my situation is, I always have something to give; even if it is just a smile.*

A wise man is reported to have said, "If a person was able to see the blessing that one receives for giving charity, the recipient of the charity would become jealous."

You would be amazed at the staggering number of people with mental illnesses who, instead of being treated, are medicated and warehoused in prisons across the country. Do you think they are getting the help they need, in prison?

Mr. Krochmelnik

June 2005

Right after Mr. Goh died, Mr. Krochmelnik moved in the same room. Everybody called Mr. Krochmelnik, "Red," This was because of his red hair. Mr. Krochmelnik was an interesting case to me because he and I were on the same housing unit. Though he and I ran in different circles, personal interactions were limited; when we saw each other we were cordial.

After Mr. Williams had taught me how to fry, I opened a fried chicken restaurant on the tier. Eager to actualize my entrepreneurial spirit, I had two chicken batters; Original and Special Blend. The original was made with finely ground Rice Crispies, and Special Blend was made with finely crushed nachos. Red worked in the officers' dining room and, therefore, had access to the cooking supplies that I needed for my daily operation. Thus, our relationship began.

Red used to crack me up! He has been locked up in America for 20 years and still has a heavy accent. He told me that he used to be a professional soccer player and that was how he ended up in the States. How he ended up in prison is a different matter. I think that it had involved a robbery. And although he has explained it to me several times, I still never quite understood. Whatever it was, he claimed innocence.

Like Mr. Dejesus, Red had prostate cancer, and it was spreading fast. Like Mr. Dejesus his legs swelled up like tree trunks, and it was more comfortable for him to sleep in a reclining chair. Also, like Mr. Dejesus, he had applied for Medical Clemency.

By law, a Medical Clemency 'can' be granted by the Governor after doctors have deemed a patient-prisoner terminally ill and he or she has six months or less to live. Strange as it may sound, it takes 6 months to a year to process the paperwork. That being said, it should come as no surprise that in the history of Palliative Care no person has ever been granted a Medical Clemency, regardless of how much more it costs to house terminally ill prisoners in prison.

Red wasn't officially under my care, but because we had known each other, I would often visit. Whenever I came around his face would light up like a 1000 watt bulb. He would quickly pull the oxygen mask off his face and say, "Come-come-come, sit wit meee brrrudder."

His accent reminded me of "Bullwinkle's," Boris and Natasha, and tickled me at the sound.

"What's up Red?"

His whole expression would change and he would whisper "Zay ar trrrying to keeel me," and look around like somebody else was in the room.

Somehow, I got sucked right into that crap! He had me looking around, paranoid, like a crack head hiding from somebody he had stolen from.

"Who's trying to kill you?" I whispered in return.

"Za gobberrrment." Then he leaned back in his chair, like he just passed off some valuable intelligence.

Still whispering, yet desperately wanting to laugh, I asked, "Why is the government trying to kill you?"

"I don't know." Then he reached for a pack of Newports.

Red had a thin white sheet covering his lap that had gravitated between his thighs, exposing his huge freckled legs and feet. From the waist down he looks like "Fat Bastard" from the Austin Powers movies.

"Keep da money; keep da Mojo, Gemme da baby!"

He had told me that his family was arranging for him to be released to Israeli custody, and from there he could get the best medical treatment in the world. He sounded very optimistic, and I figured that if anyone had a shot at Clemency it would be him.

Everyday I came pass he would call me to the room. I don't care who was in there, he would stop in mid-sentence, dismissing them and welcoming me in. He didn't want me to get coffee, clean up, or anything from the kitchen; he genuinely just enjoyed my presence. Sometimes I would just sit in there and do my homework.

I would wheel him out to the courtyard so he could get some fresh air and a smoke, but he didn't like being around other people so he would smoke in the room. Other than the fact that you're not supposed to smoke indoors in prison, (another joke), Red was on oxygen. He had a huge oxygen tank right next to him that read "Highly Flammable" in big red letters. Red would not only be sitting right next to it, smoking, but he would actually have the mask around his neck!

I would vehemently refuse to enter the room if and when he would smoke. So whenever I came around he would quickly throw the cigarette in the toilet and ask me to sit and talk.

A Russian guy named Boris (no relation to the one from Bullwinkle) was housed on Phase II and had approached me about Red. He said their mothers knew each another and asked if I could get a message to him, which I did. I even arranged for him to come to E.C.U. to visit.

That's another good thing about Palliative Care; if you have a relative who is also in South Woods, they will permit a visit. He wasn't a relative but I managed, through the Grace of GOD, to get permission for him to come to see him.

During this period of time in my life, I cringed from the pangs of Islamphobia and anti-Islamic sentiment across the globe. One thing I had never factored is the *prejudice many African American Christians have towards Muslims, which I probably never would have imagined had it not been for the Monday Morning Meetings.*

My grandfather told me how, when he was in World War II, European Americans told European Women that African Americans have tails! I assumed that people who themselves have been subjected to prejudices and false propagandas would be more conscious and understanding.

On top of that, it appeared to me that the whole world is attacking Muslims with impunity, and nobody cares. I watched a documentary on PBS about the Jewish settlers and the wall that is being built to section off Palestine. I couldn't believe my eyes or my ears. One settler said, with M-16 in hand, "I don't believe in building this wall because they will think that it is okay to build up to it. Rather, my wall is as far as this bullet will travel."

The next day I came in feeling depressed and disillusioned. Red called me and demanded that I come in the room. Big Tommy, Red's volunteer, was in the room sitting at the only other available chair. Red didn't like his volunteer and motioned for him to leave. Red told me, "He shteeels (steals) and I don't trrrush (trust) heem arrround." He said, "You arrre zee only one I trrrush."

He gave me the combination to his lock and asked me to go into his locker and get his photo album because he wanted to show me some pictures. I cracked up at him wearing these little white and green striped shorts, with socks that came up to his knees.

"Man, Red you had a bald spot when you were twenty?" I joked

He unconsciously reached for the baseball cap that he was rarely seen without. In fact, I honestly didn't know that Red was bald in the middle until he came to the program. It was khaki brown to match our uniforms. But from years of constant usage it was faded in spots like sand fatigues and had more patches than a Slaves' quilt.

As he flipped through the pages of his past I could see glimmers of life in his eyes, like sparklers during the Fourth of July. These were obviously happier times and I couldn't help but wonder where would he be had he not caught this charge.

He showed me a picture of his mother. She was in a cluttered kitchen, looking like an old Italian lady in a Ragu commercial. He showed me his brothers, all of whom had full heads of dark hair, where his red hair and freckles came from I refused to ask. Then he showed me his sister. She was blonde, beautiful, like the American girl of the 70's. I never saw a father but I suspected there was more than one.

Then he flipped to a page towards the back. He was in uniform, looking proud and disciplined. He was in an Israeli uniform and he was holding an M-16. My face just dropped. All I could imàgine was what I saw on the program the night before. All I could think of was Red killing and oppressing defenseless Muslim men, women and children.

My heart was filled with rage! I wouldn't have felt much different if I were caring for an old White man and he pulled out some pictures of him wearing his white KKK sheets and hood.

I tried not to show it, but Red picked up on it immediately, and said, "Brrrudder, seeet down."

I sat down quietly. He reached his hand out and touched my face, not much differently than my grandfather would have, smiled, and then he shook his head as if he were remembering things that had happened at another time in his life and told me, "In life, people wear many different uniforms. And while wearing these uniforms we may do things that we are not proud of, in the cause of something that we have no control over. However, when we take the uniforms off, we are all the same."

He then reached for my necklace and gently caressed the medallion; a Star & Crescent. Then he grabbed the collar of my shirt and said, "Brrrudder, in here, we wear da same uniform. We are all we have."

An immediate smile erupted across my face and the constricting realities of a world full of hate evaporated like summer rain on a hot tin roof. Red and I enjoyed each

84

other's company for the rest of the day. I must have laughed a thousand times. He died that evening. Rest in Peace.

The only means of destroying the hatred and animosity amongst people of different religious faiths is removing the uniforms of intolerance and recognizing that the essence of all our faiths mandate humane-ness.

'Humane' comes from the Latin words 'homo' (Man) and 'humus' (soil) referring to the origins of our physical bodies (i.e. Earth); it means having what are considered the 'best' qualities of MANKIND!; kindness, tenderness, mercifulness, consideration, ect... War is not on that list! Terrorism is not on that list! Oppression is not on that list!

In Michael Bradley's book, "the Columbus Conspiracy," at the close of Chapter Three: "Godfroi de Bouillion wanted to create a New Jerusalem in the Holy Land where the three great faiths of the West could be reconciled. He failed, but this sort of crusade is apparently what motivated Chrisopher Columbus and his supporters and financial backers. His voyage may have been a crusade to establish a 'New Jerusalem in a New World' and, I think, this is the light in which we should view his motivations. It is also a perspective and a light that will permit some insight into the anomalous facts and unlikely coincidences of his life. He seems to have been a part of an ancient, noble conspiracy to create a world of religious toleration between Jew, Christian, and Muslims, a New

Jerusalem. That, I think, was Columbus' concept of a crusade, and the only worthwhile kind of crusade."

Mr. McKenzie

After Red passed, an odd fellow by the name of McKenzie moved into that room. Mr. McKenzie, like Red, was not my patient. My patient's name was Mr. Rivera. He was a very proud Puerto Rican and every time I came to help, he refused, so I would visit other people.

McKenzie was a middle aged African American with a paper bag brown complexion and a sense of humor that was as vast as his smile. I don't recall what was ailing him, probably because he never complained, but I know it was caused by a life of drug abuse.

He and I would sit and talk, and he would give me the current events of E.C.U. If you think General Hospital has scandal, try prison hospital and you'll truly be entertained. A guy in a walker got into a fight with a guy in a wheelchair and McKenzie described the fight blow for blow better than Howard Cosell. The guy in the walker had the height advantage and peppered the guy in the wheelchair with a flurry of weak right hand jabs until the I.V. in his left arm got tangled forcing him to lean over to untangle them. That was all that the powerful arms of the guy in the wheelchair needed to knock the guy in the walker out!

In the mornings, before it got too hot, we would sit in the courtyard and enjoy the sun. McKenzie didn't smoke either, so we would have to find a corner where no one was smoking just to get fresh air, outdoors! After finding a space he would talk about his favorite nurses. Nurse Joyce who worked upstairs, and nurse Charlie who worked downstairs. Joyce is a sweet lady who is extremely top heavy, even larger than Ms. Johnson. McKenzie claims there is scientific proof that female hormones are pumped into cows and transfers through their milk, and that is what caused Ms. Joyce and Ms. Johnson's breasts to grow that big.

"Yeah, alright man."

"I'm serious King, I saw it on the..." he was caught in mid-sentence as Ms. Charlie walked by, looking like a chocolate Easter bunny. "Umm-um!" McKenzie interrupted with his fist balled up and then screamed, "Drum sticks, candy yams, sweet potatoes pie, and cranberry sauce!"

I don't know where that came from, but I understood what he meant. Her dark chocolate complexion was so smooth that it shined. Though she is short, thick, and not the stereotypical beauty, her style, pizzazz, personality, and self-confidence made her undeniably attractive. Plus, if you can catch her by herself, she is definitely nice to be around.

No one understands the extent of my struggles!

"Get your mind out the gutter Mr. McKenzie."

"Shoot, I'm dying but I ain't dead!"

Mr. McKenzie made my day, and anytime that I felt down I could stop past and I was guaranteed a laugh.

As his condition worsened, it became necessary for him to go to a hospital outside of the prison to assist in his care. He liked the trips because he'd get to see more nurses. He told me that "I was lying in the hospital bed daydreaming about a girl I saw on Springer, I was in the audience screaming, 'Take it off!' and a gorgeous young nurse came in. I must have looked really bad because she started feeding me." He grimaced as he imagined what he must have looked like, and then continued, "I was about to tell her I don't need your help. Until she told me that as soon as she finishes feeding me she's going to give me a sponge bath." He was grinning from ear to ear, "You should have seen me in there acting like I can't move my arms."

"Man, you crazy!"

"That ain't all. About an hour later, I purposely pooped myself, just so she could come back and do it again."

"What did she say?"

"She didn't say nothing. They sent this big fat lady who looked like the woman from 'Misery'."

He looked at me with disgust. "She had these big old clown hands." Then turned to see if anyone could hear what he was about to say, and whispered, "Don't tell nobody, but I think she molested me."

88

By now, was laughing so hard my face hurt and I got the hiccups!

"That's okay, now I know what time she goes on break, I guarantee that won't not happen again!"

That's when my assigned patient, Mr. Rivera, walked over and politely excused himself for interfering into our conversation. In a Spanish accent, more by choice than his inability to speak clear English, he said, "Pardon me, but uh, what's your name?"

"They call me Mr. King but you can call me Qawi." (My Islamic name is Abdul Qawi) "Qawi?" He squinted his face like he sucked on something sour. "That sounds like a bird!"

"What?" I interjected.

"That's what I'll call you... Bird." and then he walked away.

Mr. McKenzie was cracking up!

As the things were coming to a head in my life outside of E.C.U. I began writing a "Hood" book as a response to all the books that were floating around without substance. I wanted to make a positive difference, but I realized that if you feed a baby steak, he will never be able to digest it. So my approach to this was to give all the things the younger generations love; drugs, sex, and violence, while at the same time leaving positive messages, educational tidbits, and food for thought. I think that I did an excellent job. **(Look for '1MannTeam' online or at a book store near you.)**

Unfortunately, I carelessly left a chapter that happened to have a sex scene inside the printer. Mrs. Golden, the computer lab teacher, found it, beat me up, and forbade me from using the computers in the same capacity. I tried to explain, but she wasn't hearing it. And, the manipulative Muslim brother, whose name I will not mention, caught wind of this and spread the word that I was writing a porno book!

On the bright side of the scenario, this gave me more free time, and since I was able to come and go to E.C.U. pretty much as I pleased, I enjoyed this freedom to the fullest. This was a double edged sword, because when you put young, healthy, vibrant, handsome, robust, potent pheromone-emitting and sexually deprived men in close proximity to females, (who by nature of mathematics, are at an utter disadvantage with the male-female ratio, and are now receiving the attention they do not get at home) you have a mean combination.

No one understands the extent of my struggles!

Mr. McKenzie's condition deteriorated to the point that he needed a wheelchair. For the fun of it, I would pop wheelies and speed-ride him all around the E.C.U. One morning I had to take him to see the doctor. When he came out, his face was squinted and one eye was closed like he'd bitten into a sour apple. He didn't say anything so I just rode him outside and left for the day. There was a flu bug floating around and I had caught it.

I'm cynical when it comes to that whole flu season stuff. I think it's a big scam! The pharmaceutical industry is controlled by major corporations whose goals are to make profits. There is more money in remedying symptoms than finding cures. That's common sense. Do you honestly believe there is no cure for the common cold, or A.I.D.S. for that matter?

Four days later, I returned to E.C.U. and stopped to see Mr. McKenzie. He was in a corner of the room, wrapped in blankets, and with his head down.

"McKenzie!" I called out.

He picked his head up, smiled, squinted his face, and rocked back and forth like he was on the toilet having a rough bowel movement.

"What's up Bird?" he said with a strained laugh.

"What's up with you? Up in here looking like 'Mum-Ra' from the Thundercats."

He remembered the cartoon and immediately went into his rendition of the character. "Ancient spirits of evil, transform this decayed form into Mum-Ra the Ever living!" He raised his arms like he was going to stand then slumped back over and started coughing uncontrollably.

I didn't know if I should laugh or go pat him on the back.

91

"You alright?"

"As alright as I'm gonna be." Still coughing.

"Why are you squinting your face?"

"I can't help it."

"What?"

"Remember you took me to the doctor last week?"

"Yeah."

"Well, he called me in and gave me a shot."

"Okay"

"The needle was so big that when he stuck me in the butt cheek it hurt so bad that I couldn't even scream! It was there, but no sound came out. All I could do was squint my face, and I ain't been able to straighten it out since!"

We both laughed but I couldn't help but be displeased with the way the room looked and smelled. So I got behind him and took McKenzie out for his favorite sport; girl watching. After pushing him around the halls for about 20 minutes we came back to the room.

Nurse Charlie had cleaned up and was in the process of making his bed. We stopped at the door, just as she bent over to tuck the sheets, and it appeared as if everything was in slow motion.

No one understands the extent of my struggles!

McKenzie yelled, "Drum sticks, candy yams, sweet potato pie, and cranberry sauce!", and we all burst into laughter.

He died the next morning.

From Mr. McKenzie I learned that no matter how bad the situation, I can find humor in it, and when this is done, you will enjoy 'your' life, good or not so good, until the last breath.

Mr. Rivera

I was assigned Mr. Rivera in late Spring of 2005. He's a butter-pecan, raven black push back hair-do wearing, slick-talking, Salsa singing, Puerto Rican. He was very neat, clean and conscious of his appearance. He was also proud. He wouldn't become rude, but I could tell that he didn't particularly appreciate help from anyone, and I respected that.

Besides, in prison, if a guy comes and attempts to get all "Joe Familiar" with you, they are automatically looked at with skepticism. The first thing that comes to mind is that there is a scam involved. And the second is that the guy's gay. Either way, I understood his apprehension.

After a few months of coming in, everyday, greeting him and asking if he needed anything, then leaving so as not to invade his space, he began to open up a little.

He came out one morning while I was sitting with one of the non-palliative residents housed in E.C.U. by the name of Sal. Sal is an old Mobster that speaks very little English and even that sounds Italian.

"Hey Bird!" he yelled as he came over, grabbed me by the arm, and pulled me inside.

The courtyard of the E.C.U. is shaped like an octagon. There was a huge observation window behind the officers' front desk. On either side of the desk is an entrance leading outside to the courtyard. On the opposite side of the entrances, and in front of the desk, are two padded rooms, usually used for mentally ill patients who have run amuck.

As Mr. Rivera dragged me indoors my vision struggled to re-adjust to the light. While I began to get my focus, I noticed a huge man standing in the doorway of a padded room used for those who are on suicide watch. We eyed each other, as if we both looked familiar to the other, but neither of us spoke.

Once in his room, Mr. Rivera pulled his pants down to his knees, exposing his private parts, and said, "Look!"

I started to knock him upside his head, but something in his eyes told me to do as he asked.

In the crease between the upper part of the inside of his thigh and pubic area, a large dark purple lump stood out like a plumb that had been surgically implanted just under his flesh. He said it was a tumor.

Right under the tumor is a hole that would not, or could not heal. The hole must have been connected to the bladder because whenever he used the restroom, urine would pour out of the hole.

"Look at me, Bird, it leaks when I take a leak." Then he looked at me in disgust and said, "I have to sit down and pee like a woman!"

I was going to tell him that it is customary for Muslim men to sit down or squat when we urinate, but something told me this wouldn't be a good time.

He gingerly pressed his fingers down just below the tumor as if massaging a sore muscle, and a yellowish, translucent discharge of urine and puss began to ooze down his leg.

I was speechless.

"They are using radiation for the cancer...but-but the radiation, its eating through my skin," Mr. Rivera cried.

My heart really went out to him. Not just because of the physical pain he suffered, which was enormous, but for the hopelessness in his eyes; that utterly debilitating blanket of despair. The uncomfortable nothingness; a place where you are totally drained and at the same time unable to sleep.

I was able to recognize and empathize with Mr. Rivera's feelings because I too struggled with bouts of depression, and in fact, was wrestling with depression at that time; a state where I have often used alcohol, drugs, aggression, or women to escape. Unconsciously, I began to use the latter; women.

For me, once Pandora's Box was open I was off to the races. I became more brazen in my entertaining of the females who work in the prison. Entertainment that did not necessarily led to outright sex, yet the underlining

96

current was so filled with innuendos that if the opportunity presented itself, I had no doubt as to the outcome.

No one understands the extent of my struggles!

July 14, 2005

Mr. Rivera's wounds have become infected. He hasn't slept or eaten since I left him yesterday. He says he is in too much pain to sleep and wants the administration to send him to the hospital for better treatment. I can dig it.

July 15, 2005

The hole on the inside of his leg has become limpid and crusted along the edges. The hole's opening looking like an albino scab had developed over it. He's still got swagger, and lots of pride, which makes it even more difficult to watch the hope slowly slip away.

Today Ms. Johnson asked if I would be willing to extend my services to a gentleman who's in a coma. She says he's not dying, so it not actually Palliative Care, but the doctors claim he is likely brain dead.

July 26, 2005

Today, for the first time, Mr. Rivera didn't run me off. In fact, he asked me to stay. His room hadn't been cleaned in 3 days and it smelled horrible! But I was honored to do so. After I finished, Mr. Rivera, with the look of a man struggling to get up after fighting Mike

Tyson in his eyes, told me that he loves me, and if his muscles were not so weak he would never need me to clean for him. He still is very proud. And I admired him for that.

July 27, 2005

Now, to spare his pride, instead of asking Mr. Rivera if he wanted my help, I'd just come in and start cleaning. As I cleaned, Nurse Dawn, the one who almost caught a beat down from Mr. Goh, walked in. She's a middle aged woman with a kind of dumpy build, pasty white, and mouse brown hair. But she is sweet, kind, has beautiful greenish hazel eyes, and from the back, depending on the angle, looked almost like she had a Black girl's booty; Almost. I've been locked up too long!

"Dawn, can you do me a favor?" I cautiously asked

She turned and stood within inches of my face and asked, "What do you want?"

(DANGER! DANGER! DANGER! Will Robinson!)

She shook my cool a little with that. We've interacted before; I never paid her much thought. Nevertheless, I may have left an encounter with her, wondering if she threw a pass, and then dismissing it as delusional, this was the first time I knew for sure. Though my voice cracked and raised a few octaves, I managed to regain my swagger and said, "As you can smell, it stinks."

98

She shook her head in affirmation, "Mr. Rivera can't help it, but he's constantly pooping up some stuff that smells like old rotten chitterlings, [pig intestine] and nobody wants to be around him."

I thought Mr. Rivera was asleep but I noticed his shoulders cringe in shame from my words.

"Uh-ah," she seductively replied.

"I need you to bring some oils in for me."

"What kind of oils?"

I knew I had her then.

"The kind that the Muslims wear."

"Oh!" she exclaimed as she folded up one of Mr. Rivera's shirts.

"Can you handle that for me?"

She abruptly turned around and bent over at the waist to pick something off the ground that I had seen her drop seconds before, lightly pressing her soft derriere against me and returned, "Can you handle that for me?" Then she giggled and pretended that she was playing.

No one understands the extent of my struggles.

I have been in leadership of our religious community for years, and I've given numerous sermons on the vices of fornication and adultery. I knew I had no business doing what I was doing.

Can you imagine how much of a straight-up hypocrite I felt like? Can you imagine how I felt walking around and feeling like everyone can see my shame?

At the same time, I was lonely, desperate, and wanted to feel love from somebody [heterosexually of course] even if the love was out of nothing at all.

I had to throw that in there because, for some reason, people have the misconception that men come to prison and turn gay. Sure you have gay men in prison, but they were gay before they got here. Prison just gave some of them the opportunity to express it.

The devil exploited my weaknesses and my longings; hard and heavy.

She wore different faces;

came from different races;

wore different uniforms;

and popped up in different places.

I knew it was wrong, but like Jamie Fox, in the movie 'Ray',I couldn't leave without a little taste. Once I plunged the needle in, the devil had me hooked. Like a crack-head stealing money out his mothers' pocket book.

As soon as the high was gone, the pain was twice as great!

And I had twice the troubles!

I'll tell you once again,

"No one understands the extent of my struggles!"

My life became deeply engrossed in the activities of E.C.U. during this period, and since I cared for Mr. Rivera in the mornings and Mr. Williford in the afternoons, bear with me as their stories and mine, entwine.

August 1, 2005

Today we had our Monday Morning Meeting and two civilian guests came. They are volunteering to sit with patients from 9:00 a.m. to 11:30 a.m. on Mondays. That's cool. They seemed like very nice people. Plus, 9 o'clock is when we normally have our meeting. It will be nice to have someone with our guys until we return.

During the meeting, Ms. Johnson informed us that Mr. Paterson, one of our longest lasting palliative care patients, was to be placed on a vigil. Mr. Tarr, a young white guy, who was one of our newest members, and the first Buddhist, was Mr. Patterson's volunteer and was taking it pretty badly.

I felt proud to know that I was instrumental in breaking the religious barrier in Palliative Care, and the group has since accepted more people from different religious perspectives.

After the meeting I lingered behind to talk to Ms. Johnson because she said she had something she wanted to tell me. I was forming my company using original inspirational poems that were written by people in prison called, "Inside Inspirations."

[Go to www.insideinspiration.com for more info]

I figured that this would be the perfect time to test my target market.

"Ms. Johnson!" I said, attempting to pry her away from whatever she was gibber-jabbing about and gain her undivided attention.

She reached over and pinched the crap out of me and said, "Now I know yo momma taught you better manners than interrupting when grown folks are talking."

"Oouch! Ms. Johnson."

"I sure am tired of hearing you calling my name. What you want? Wit yo big head self."

"I got yo big head," I shot back.

"I doubt it," she shot back even faster.

"Check this out," I said as I handed her my cards.

"You're the one who said you wanted to see me."

At first her face showed signs of annoyance, then curiosity, and then a smile covered her chubby chocolate cheeks. Her skin glows! I wonder what she tastes...nah I'm buggin for real now.

As she handed the stack of cards back, she said, "I like that one, I could give that to my daughter," and started to walk off.

102

"Hold up, there's more," sensing a possible sale.

"I don't have time right now, Mr. King."

I pulled the stops and hit her with my puppy dog look. She smiled and said, "Okay, bring them this afternoon when you come to see Mr. Williford. That's what I wanted to talk to you about." She paused to see if I had any objections, and continued, "I'll look at them then, okay?"

"You've got a date."

"No, you don't...Mr. King." Then she punched me in the chest and walked out.

Afterwards I went back to see Mr. Rivera. He had just received news that his appeal to the Federal Courts for a Habeas Corpus was denied because of a technicality. This was the coup de grace, the straw that broke the camel's back, his last hope to get out and get better medical treatment.

I noticed the growing sense of helplessness in his eyes. A feeling that, despite being locked up for a number of years and subjected to the often arbitrary whims of an unjust judicial system and its officers, he still was not used to, and he was terrified.

This is when Mr. Rivera broke down and told me his story. Sitting on the edge of his bed, wearing an old Wife Beater that was ripped under the right arm, and some cut off sweat pants, he looked up at me and said,

"Bird, I had just been accepted into a triple A minor league baseball team!" He paused for a second, lowered his head, then raised it back up and continued, "I had just flown here to the States. Miami...beautiful women! Have you ever been to Florida?" I knew it was rhetorical "My sister moved to New Jersey from the Island and I hadn't seen her in some years, so, I caught the bus here to Jersey to visit before training camp began."

You could see the look of pride on his face as he reminisced. After drinking the last of his coffee he continued, stressing his Spanish accent, sounding and looking like Scarface, "A couple of years...after a couple of years I could have made it to the majors."

After saying that, he walked around a bit, strutting with his chest stuck out and continued, "I use to be good-- real good, and fast...like lightening," raising his voice towards the end of the sentence, as if in a Shakespearean play. "My position was short-stop and although I may not have been a heavy home run hitter, I could place the ball anywhere on the field I wanted."

"Well, what happened?" I earnestly asked.

"A robbery occurred, and whoever it was, da gringos said I fit the description. I could barely speak English, and ended up getting railroaded!" he said, while hitting his fist into the palm of his hand. "Come to find out, the guy who committed the robbery was an African American who was 6'1" and weighed 250 pounds. That sounds more like you than me! I even had a bus ticket stub that proved I was still on the bus coming up here when the crime was committed."

"Whoa," I interjected.

"What, you think Hurricane Carter is the only one wrongfully convicted in New Jersey? This is the most corrupt State in America! It's all about the money." Tears began to well in his eyes. "That was 15 years ago, now they don't want to let me go because they know that I am going to sue!"

He neglected to file for Certification. This is the process where you file to the State Supreme Court for relief. They'll usually rubber stamp whatever the Appellate Division says, but it still is a cog in the machine. So, no matter how meritorious your claim is, you will be shot down.

"Right is right and wrong is wrong, right?"

"Uh--I guess," slightly confused by his question.

"I never rob nobody in my life! These Gringos know I didn't rob nobody, I have proof, but they won't accept it because I didn't do something that I didn't know I had to do. That's wrong, right?"

That's definitely wrong. And although I'll be the first to say America is the greatest Country on Earth, we still have a lot of work to do, collectively. Justice should not be *predicated upon race or financial standings. Right-is-right and wrong is wrong, Right?*

"Caged Bird"

Vol. 1

Written by Jack Duford

a.k.a

Wile E. Giggles

"No One Can Understand the Extent of My Struggles"

I was brought up the hard way,

It brought me to Southwoods-Rahway,

Twenty-three hour lockdowns, sitting in my cell all day,

Anyway, I worked in Palliative Care,

I volunteered; they got the sickest prisoners there,

I met a man named Red, who made me more aware,

Because the uniforms we wear n how we shouldn't compare,

Cuz, we're all the same,

Got screwed by the game,

The bars raw our brain,

I maintain,

N focus on my sanity,

Cuz the enemy took me from my family,

Try to forgive myself, but these walls are closing in,

I'm feelin so cold like the winter's frozen wind,

Many prisoners lost, but I chose to win,

Met a wise man named McKenzie,

Fate brought me close to him,

I used to do dirt so people would desire me,

Now I see it's better for them to admire me,

I will become the MAN I'm tryin to be,

No matter how hard or how it tires me,

My philosophy is my problem is me,

No negativity, is that positive, probably,

Now I'm destined to win N no one's stopping me,

This too shall pass n my faith they can't rob from me,

The system is twisted, too many brothers incarcerated,

They paid their way for prison, but never educated em,

Sedated the brightest minds,

Medicated wit crooked spines,

Noddin out rottin now,

Dedicated to tellin lies,

I seek refuge from the Lord of the Rising Sun,

The battle has begun, dry your eyes my Cryin Son,

No more buyin bundles,

Or lustful thoughts that puzzle,

No one understands the extent of my struggles,

I extend my helpin hand, cuz I'm young n healthy,

To help the elderly,

N find you don't need money to be wealthy,

I've seen death firsthand; he'll need a coroner soon,

I felt it stand behind me in the corner of the room,

It made it so cold, I couldn't even breathe,

It came for the dyin, now is his time to be retrieved,

I called him Mr. White, n he said it's Mr. Green,

I'll never forget the sight; I could clearly paint the scene,

When I'm doin right, I don't need to sleep to dream,

I watched his eyes close to follow the light beam,

Gone to the better place, sleep now you're tired,

It made me a better man, my brain's been re-wired,

I hope it never stops, I hope it takes me higher,

N puts me in position to motivate and inspire,

Who will pass on my legacy?

If I die now,

Would I be remembered as an Enemy?

I'm tryin so hard to change,

And calm my violent tendencies,

But my conscience is hard to bear,

When it's rambling on endlessly,

Just remember me, as a mortar and a king,

Don't take life for granted, you could be anything,

Harness your talents if you love to draw or sing,

Don't waste your life chasin money and diamond rings,

Inferior materialism ain't livin,

*The ones who really care about you only want the love
your giving,*

Escape from hell become more than an Empty shell,

Fill the hole wit knowledge, why not? Might as well,

Put down the L cuz ya quickly burnin out,

*The Devil's a pimp in the drugs are a bitch he's turnin
out,*

He wants us all as tricks,

That's how he gets his kicks,

Gives us a couple of licks,

Then makes us need a fix,

110

He wants us all broken, so we need his hands to help us,

But he don't give a fuck about us,

He's egotistical and selfish,

I don't need him no more,

I don't want the trouble,

No one understands,

The extent of my struggle.

Later that afternoon I went to see Mr. Williford. I had to check in at the desk upstairs. Officer Riggins was working the post. He patted me down, and searched my belongings. Then he stood in my face, looked at my necklace, and told me that I have to tuck it inside my shirt; not because of regulation but because it represents Islam.

Of course, I wasn't going to tuck anything, and I began to feel the adrenaline rushing through my body, but Ms. Johnson came out and saved the day.

"Mr. King, I'm glad to see you made it. Officer Riggins, Mr. King will be coming to visit Mr. Williford in the afternoons."

Ms. Johnson had a little juice around here so he stood down. "Now, let me show you your new job," she said while punching me in the back.

She took me to the room where Mr. Williford was. The room's a lot larger than any room I've seen in prison. It even has its own shower.

Mr. Williford laid there, eyes open but paying us no attention. He had all sorts of tubes and gadgets connected to him; one in his arm, one in his stomach, one in his penis, and one in his throat. The respirator made this strange sound like somebody breathing through a voice box, "Luke, I am your father" or an astronaut's transmission.

Colonel Steve Austin, astronaut, a man barely alive. We can rebuild him. We have the technology. We have the

112

capabilities to build the world's first bionic man. We can make him better than he was before; better, stronger, faster.

"Mr. King!" Ms. Johnson pinched me on the side.

"Oouch!"

"Did you hear what I said?"

"Yeah Ms. Johnson, why you buggin?"

She had a habit of hitting and pinching, she will even throw stuff at you. A couple times I started to pluck her upside the head, but I knew it was her way of showing love.

"Well Mr. King, I'm gone, some of us have work to do."

"Before you go, check these out," and I handed her my cards.

There was one of those hospital tables that are shaped like the letter C. The base goes under the bed while the top comes across for those that are bed ridden. She placed the poem on top and began to read. Her little chubby face would light up when she read a line she liked. And I felt a sense of pride and accomplishment when my work is approved of in this manner.

Most of my cards are inspirational poems printed on decorative backgrounds and laminated. I even personalize. All one has to do is give me a few particulars and I'll write a masterpiece, tailor fit, for you. [Sometimes

I include the personal ones that I have written if they can be used for a general market. At the end of the stack was one such card. I tried to remove it before she got to it but I was too late. It's a poem entitled, "If I were the water of your bath."

As I said before, Ms. Johnson's a big girl, so sometimes her breathing gets a little heavy. I'm used to that, but her breathing became so heavy she had to sit down. I wasn't sure if it was good or bad, but she was holding the card in front of her with both hands and began to read the card slowly.

When she stood back up, two large protrusions made it impossible not to notice that she must have really enjoyed it. She stayed awhile longer; we talked and took the opportunity to get to know each other better than I thought we would.

No one understands the extent of my struggles.

August 2, 2005

The next morning, I stopped to see Mr. Rivera, all the macho crap was out the window, and he broke down like a slot machine. He, too, believes that if he could just get out to the streets he could get better treatment.

"Bird, if I had money, they would do something for me."

"You're probably right," I returned as I headed out the door.

August 3, 2005

Two more civilians began volunteering for Palliative Care today, another elderly married couple and, even though the man looks just like Grandpa Walton, they've been together for so long they look alike. It must be nice to grow old with the one you love, and still do things together. That's living!

August 5, 2005

I came in this morning to clean up for Mr. Rivera, and ran back out A.S.A.P. to beat the heat. I had to return at 1:00 p.m. to see Mr. Williford. The heat and humidity outside today was deadly. Nobody was out, nobody but me, and it's so hot that I can see vapors dancing on the ground like Venusian belly dancers. By the time I finish my seemingly unending expedition across the desert sands of the Hijaz, my eyes were burning and I felt like a flame-broiled Whopper.

When I walked into the E.C.U., strangely, the cooler air caused me to sweat more. Either that or it was so hot that my sweat was evaporating before it rolled off my head.

I went straight upstairs and as soon as I came out of the stairway I was greeted by a snarling face. Officer Riggins was staring at me hard, stern, and menacingly. My instincts warned of danger, but if I were to turn now I would look suspicious. So I continued, and though I did not return a hostile stare, I refused to lower my sights; I held my head up high. Whatever happens I will maintain manliness!

The closer I got, the more I felt like I was in a staring contest waiting to see which one will blink first. He did. As I reached to hand him my I.D. and briefcase, he averted his sight towards my necklace.

He rummaged through my briefcase, made me empty my pockets, frisk-searched me, and while patting me down said, "I thought I told you to tuck that chain?"

I didn't answer, but I noticed his partner easing in from my peripheral. Naturally, my muscles tense, my heart rate quickens, and I'm preparing for battle.

"Now get the fuck outta here!" Officer Riggins screamed from behind me.

I turned to face him, bewildered.

"You heard what I said!"; Standing within inches of my face.

I head butted him so hard dark blood came gushing forth like the rivers that swept through New Orleans. I followed up with an uppercut, left jab, and crumbled him with a right hook.

His partner touched me on the shoulders, awakening me from my daydream, and said, "Alright King, see you tomorrow."

I was pissed, but not stupid, so I turned, tucked my tail, and headed back out into the blazing sun.

August 6, 2005

For the first time since I've been coming over here, Officer Evans greeted me as I put my I.D. on the desk.

"Good morning, King."

"Good morning to you both," I returned.

Officer Goldborough, with her fine self, didn't say anything. She was just smiling like she knew something I did not.

I got about halfway down the hall, smelled a horrid scent, and I noticed how all the residents were holding their noses, and grumbling under their breaths. Before I even made it to Mr. Rivera's room the smell was so pungent that I had to stop. My eyes were watering. I

117

thought about turning and going back but everyone was at the desk, looking at me to see my reaction. Damn!

He was sitting on the toilet, without a single stitch of clothing on, and the door wide open! Naturally I begin to back pedal to give him some privacy but he caught me before I could get away.

"Bird! Hold up, don't leave."

"Man, I don't want to be in here while you're taking a dump!"

"Bird, I can't help it," he pleaded, with tears flowing in streams. Then continued, "And nobody will come around me because I stink!"

I never could stand to see a grown man cry. So, to make things more bearable, I pulled out a bottle of Kush fragrance oil that Dawn had brought me and poured some on a piece of tissue. Then I rolled it up and lit one end. That's a prison version of incense.

"You want some coffee?" I asked after setting my briefcase down and headed towards the kitchen.

"Thank you, Bird... I love you man."

"Don't be getting mushy and stuff on me while you're butt-naked. I'm Muslim; we don't get down like that!"

He smiled and nodded his head in affirmation.

"I'll be back in a minute, so put some clothes on."

118

When I stepped out everyone seemed to be looking at me intensely, watching, waiting for some sign of disapproval, dismay, or disgruntledness. I smiled and kept it moving as if there was nothing going on out of the normal.

By the time I returned, the strong, dark, aromatic liquid counterbalanced the rancid bowels of Mr. Rivera enough for us to both enjoy a cup of coffee and a laugh.

I couldn't help but think of the sisters in Africa who suffer from fistulas, many of whom have been ostracized because of a medical condition that they have no control over. Fistulas are often the result of young girls having children too early or the lack of proper medical treatment.

After cleaning up Mr. Rivera's room a bit, I felt compelled to give him a hug and say, "I love you too, old man." After a brief embrace, he pushed me away and said, "Don't be gettin' all mushy on me!" and we both laughed.

At this stage, I could tell that he has accepted his fate. In most cases, when a patient gets to this point, he's usually more at peace. And I was grateful that he had become so. For the following few weeks I watched as his life reached Fruition, and gained a greater understanding of the passage, written by Langston Hughes, and used by many, known as, The Serenity Prayer: "GOD, grant me the serenity to accept the things I cannot change, the *courage to change the things that I can, and the wisdom to know the difference."*

August 12, 2005

Today has been super-long! 8:00 a.m. to 9:00 a.m. with Mr. Rivera, who is no longer conscious, but still poops non-stop, 9:00 a.m. to 10:30 a.m. in the Monday Meeting. Deacon Jim took over for Deacon Pachelli, who was fired because somebody from a prisoner's family met him at church. [I thought that's what a Deacon is supposed to do.] Deacon Jim is as kind and gentle as a lamb, but his meetings are so boring that after a half-hour everyone is fighting to stay awake. The meeting ended, and I am preparing to go watch Mr. Williford. I was stopped by the nurse practitioner who asked me to stay later. She is a tan, middle age women with a slim yet curvaceous build.

I was standing over his bed wondering what exactly I am supposed to do for this man. Moreover, I'm trying to figure out where I've seen him before. He has a perpetual stream of drool that has lightened his complexion along its course. And he appears to be looking at me, sometimes, with one eye, while the other eye travels in a different direction.

A soft, unmistakable feminine hand softly touches my back as the nurse practitioner squeezed by to gain entry. I could feel the softness of her ample breast against

120

my back. She could have taken another route or asked me to move, but women will be women.

"That's called Dolls Eye" she solemnly uttered.

"Huh?"

"It's a condition that happens to some people suffering from severe head trauma, and it usually indicates that the person is brain dead."

It was strange, because as she said that, he looked at me, and I remembered where I had seen him. He was the big guy who was in the suicide watch room when Mr. Rivera dragged me inside. I had to sit down. A chair was positioned between the foot of his bed and the door entrance. She continued to talk, but she might as well been speaking "Colonel" [Blah-blah blah-blah] because I couldn't comprehend it.

Mr. Williford was brought here because of a beef at Bayside. Often when a prisoner has an altercation with an officer from another prison and gets shipped to another prison, he'll be beaten there and wherever he is sent. When I saw him, he looked fine. So, my guess would be that the second beating must have been something terrible. That second beating would have to have happened here.

The nurse practitioner was steady fixing and adjusting the tubes connected to him, preparing to remove his oxygen mask. She had on bright yellow scrubs that were loose fitting, but she had the habit of pulling the pants up extra high so that often you can see a print in her pubic area that looked like a camel's foot. When she squatted down like a back catcher, with her legs wide open, it snapped me out of my daze. Then she stood up, leaned over at the waist, facing my direction, and picked up a piece of paper on the ground. The way her scrub top was cut, everything from the tip of her nose to her belly button was fully exposed. From that position she looked straight up into my eyes. I was a little frightened, unsure if she was intentionally exposing her goodies or if it was by accident, so I averted my gaze. But she just kept talking.

Nurse Dawn walked in and as soon as she saw her supervisor bent over her facial expression changed from a smile to a frown, and it became obvious that there was some animosity between the two.

"Hey, Mr. Williford!" Dawn cheerfully says, openly ignoring the both of us.

Okay, that's my cue to leave, so I stood and headed for the door.

"Mr. King, can you please watch him for twenty more minutes?" the Head nurse asks.

I smiled, sat back down, and she left the room.

"I can't stand her!" Dawn exclaims.

Then she did exactly what the nurse had done not five minutes before; checking tubes and stuff. I was tired, and ready to fall asleep, so I asked Dawn to watch Mr. Williford while I went downstairs to get some coffee.

By the time I made it back, Dawn was standing outside the room talking to a Spanish prisoner. He was bald with thick eyebrows that he arched like a female. I had seen him before, we had even spoken once or twice, but we didn't run in the same circles so the conversation was limited but respectful. Strangely, he's shooting me rocks [menacing stares] as I walk pass. He barely comes up to the height of my shoulders and I outweigh him by at least 50lbs. Him fighting with me would be like throwing a Chihuahua in a cage with a Pit-bull. Whatever he was going through I had nothing to do with so I kept it moving.

Mr. Williford coughs up a goobly goo of gook straight through the whole in his neck like the blow hole of a porpoise! Dawn must have heard him and came rushing back in. Little Poppi walked in behind her. She was cleaning him and Poppi was adjusting his head. Better man than me, because I wasn't getting anywhere near that.

She asked him to move Mr. Williford around for something. Though Mr. Williford had lost a lot of weight his frame was still too big for the young Latino. I would have volunteered to help, but since he shot me a rock I sat right down and pretended not to be paying attention but cracking up inside.

"Why don't you ask him to help you?" Dawn asked.

123

He looked over at her and kept tugging on the sheets under Mr. Williford, so I leaned back and crossed my legs. After about twenty minutes he still hadn't managed to move Mr. Williford where she needed. The officer called for him, saving him further embarrassment, and I politely walked over and lifted Mr. Williford where he was needed in all of five seconds.

"What's up with your boy?"

"What-what boy?" Dawn answered.

"The guy who was just shooting me rocks?"

She looked at me real crazy and changed the subject, "I got some more oils."

Yeah?"

"I'll bring them tomorrow...are you coming up here tomorrow?"

"God Willing" I replied.

"Good!"

August 13, 2005

Mr. Rivera passed during the night so I had a little free time. I was glad he passed and I was glad for the break. I'm beginning to get burned out, so I figured I'd go back to the unit, maybe play a game of chess or scrabble. On my way out the door, the officer who was Riggins's partner called me to the side and apologized for the way his partner treated me.

124

"Dude, Riggins is in the Reserves, he hurt his leg in Iraq and ever since he found out he had to go back, he's been real cranky. He's gone for now, so you should have no problems." Then he looked around and said, "We ain't all bad."

I appreciated the fact that he would even take the time to explain that to me, and though I was forced to tuck my tail under my behind and retreat from Riggins's challenges, every battle is not worth fighting.

The fact that he would feel compelled to explain that, challenges my theory of officers. Maybe what Red said about uniforms applies to police too? Maybe.

That afternoon I returned and sure enough, Riggins was gone. I placed my I.D. at the desk and waited to be pat searched but the officers looked at me like I was crazy. I picked up on the message and kept it moving. Obviously the whole pat down, borderline molestation procedure was not how they operated and I was glad.

I didn't even get the chance to sit down before Dawn entered the room. She was looking around all paranoid like a crack-head and mumbling, "Why does everybody think I'm lying? Why won't they just believe me? I'm not lying!" Then she snapped out of it as if multiple personalities were inside of her battling for control and one finally emerged victorious.

"Hey Kingy!"

125

"Uh-What's up?" Not feelin' the Kingy crap but leery of commenting.

"I got something for you."

"Oh yeah...what?" Now I'm looking around like a crack-head. Something about this chick is too weird for me to be comfortable. My Spider Sense is going crazy.

"Go stand over there first," Dawn said while pointing towards the shower.

Hesitant, I'm looking around for boobie traps or for something to jump out, but I walk over anyway. I make it to the front of the shower when I realize nothing is there.

"How do I know that you're not wearing a wire? she asked me.

"What!" sounding like lil' John.

"How do I know that you don't have a wire on under that shirt?"

Oh, she wants to see a little something. Now my Lil' John screaming, "What?', 'YEAH!', 'OKAY!', as the realization of her purpose dawned on me, forcing blood began to race to my lower extremities faster than the raging waters ripped through New Orleans after Bush had the levies blown.

After removing my khaki shirt I took off the 'Wife Beater' and tightened my stomach muscles to give the semblance of a sculptured six pack, and slowly began my strip tease. 'I'm too sexy for my..., never mind.' Judging by the excitement in her eyes, she was pleased by what she saw.

"See?" I said and began putting my shirt back on.

Looking at my crotch she said, "You still might have a wire."

It didn't take as long this time to figure out what she wanted. I turned and pulled my pants down just far enough to reveal my semi erectness. Of course this gave the appearance that it was longer and fatter than what it really is so I showed her about half.

She pulled two huge bottles of oil out that she had hidden in her jacket as if they were a stack of bills at a strip club and headed straight for me.

Looking like Elmira from the Muppet Babies she came rushing over reaching her arms around me; touching, caressing, sniffing, and tasting my flesh. I have to admit, it felt so good. Her skin was soft and smelled so clean and fresh. I wouldn't kiss her in the mouth, you have to be very special for me to do that, but I kissed her neck. It's strange that I'll stick my penis inside her vagina yet refuse to kiss.

In the whole world gone reverse, you use to talk proper but now you curse. The sun used to shine from day to day, now the whole universe is filled with gray. No respect for family or wife and disrespect is a way of life...Doug E. Fresh

127

She grabbed him from the base and squeezed. The head grew larger. She twisted and turned it, examining every contour, and then gently kissed it. Next she went down to my scrotum, closed her eyes and inhaled deeply. Satisfied with the results she performed fellatio on me like she attended private school.

My knees buckled and all in one motion she stood up, pulled her pants down to her knee, turned around, and bent over. She was dripping wet and I felt like a virgin trying to stick myself in the right orifice. Finally she reached behind and stuck it in herself.

Dawn is the type who likes to scream and make noises while in the heat of the moment but because we are no further than ten feet from the officers' desk she was forced to restrain herself. So she bit down on a clean white towel and covered her own mouth as if she didn't trust herself to be quiet.

The fear of being caught may have even added to the excitement. At least that's my story, because I didn't last half as long as I would have liked. However, after releasing a load that seems to come from the bottom of my feet, I was satisfied and she appeared the same.

"Wow! That was a lot!" she said as if amazed.

August 27, 2005

South Woods has a plantation known as the Industry or 'I' Building. In it they make all sorts of stuff; uniforms, boots, street signs, and they also prepare food to be shipped to all the prisons in the State. And require the service of hundreds of men.

On weekday mornings, legions of prisoners are corralled into enclosures and counted like chattel before being allowed to go on to the main compound. If I can get out of my unit quick enough I can ease passed the mass movement and avoid being corralled along with the troops. I hate when I do get caught because I have to be counted like the rest and it makes me feel like a Slave.

On the weekends the plantation is closed so I don't have to rush because the only prisoners out are those going to visits from their loved ones. That's another reason why I liked coming to E.C.U. on the weekends. My immediate family is in Arizona. I haven't seen my children, or had a visit, my entire time in prison. So coming to E.C.U. was my visit.

It was a joyous Saturday morning. The main compound, with its waddling geese and beautifully kept lawns, made the late summer's morning particularly glorious. A light wisp of cottony soft clouds gently rolling in oceans of powdery blue skies baptizes my face in waters of Zam-Zam and lifts it towards the heavens.

This must be how it feels...

To prostrate upon the snow covered ice caps of the mighty Mt. Kilimanjaro.

This must be how it feels...

To be drifting in a raft in the middle of the sea.

This must be what it feels...

This must be how it feels to truly be free.

Descending from my voyage, high on life and feeling almost free, I glide into E.C.U. like I'm on roller skates. Ms. Johnson is talking to Officer Elliot at the front desk. I don't know what it is, but the red lipstick Ms. Evans puts on them big luscious lips are looking sexier than ever!

"Good morning Mr. King. How are you?" Ms. Johnson asks with a pleasant smile and softness in her eyes.

"I'm fine, thanks for asking. And you?"

"I'm great, God is good," Ms. Johnson replied.

"All the time!" Officer Elliot chimed in.

"Amen," I followed, caught in the moment.

We share a brief chuckle then Ms. Johnson continued, "Mr. King, we have a new patient that I'm assigning you."

"Okay, who?"

"His name is Mr. Sumpter. I moved him from upstairs last night. He's in room 3."

By chance I had had a minor surgery on my left index finger a few days earlier and had to stay in the

E.C.U. Observation Room until the doctor cleared me for general population.

While there I was blessed with the opportunity to see his family as they left his room. It was brief, and through a barrier of Plexiglas, but it is a sight I will never forget.

Sitting on my bed, bored to death, and looking for an excuse to leave out my room and roam the halls, [Even though I know full well I'm not supposed to.] I noticed a beautiful chocolate brown young lady exiting a room across from me. She was wearing an old-school two toned baseball shirt and sweats. The sleeves were soft pink and cut mid forearm for the classic baseball look. And the inner portion of the shirt and sweats were sparkling white. She was short and petite, and although her outfit was loose fitting, her youthfully firm prodigious ornaments and curvaceous physique was difficult to conceal.

My first instinct was to throw my fishing rod out and see if I can catch. But her parents came out of the room, clutching each other for support; I had a change of heart. They too, were small individuals. Neatly dressed in conservative apparel, they were like the cutest family in the entire universe. Just looking at them makes you want to say, "Awww." I couldn't help imagining the love and warmth they felt for each other. "Aww."

It's sad to say but most of the African American guys, that are terminal, get no visits on their final days.

So in a strange way, I was proud and honored to have seen them.

After grabbing my coffee I headed to the room. It contained an adjustable bed that actually appeared to work. Its head was raised at a 40° angle, and positioned horizontally near the door's entrance. Looking at the screws and metal rods connected in the inner workings of the bed I noticed a red and white sticker that warned against sticking your hands inside. Of course my mind began imagining my hand trapped in it as it closed.

On the left side of the foot of the bed was an oxygen machine that looked like it's been in use since the 70's. Along with its constant hum and occasional ping, it had me thinking of the beginning Six Million Dollar Man. 'We can build him better than he was before; better, stronger, faster...'

And though the bed was wrinkled and unmade no one was there. I figured he may be outside having a smoke so I headed to the yard.

"How is Mr. Sumpter doing?" Ms. Johnson asked.

"I don't know."

"Didn't you go visit him?"

"I went to the room but nobody was there."

She looked at Ms. Evans then back at me. "What you mean ain't nobody in there?" She pushed me in the direction as she walked me down herself.

"Keep on bullying me and one of these days I'm a give you what you asking for," I whispered so the officer couldn't hear.

She hit me in the back of the head. WHAP! And said loud enough for Officer Elliot to hear, "You said you are going to do what to me?" and started laughing.

"Man you get on my nerves. What you doing here on Saturday anyway?"

"Boy you too young to have nerves." she returned, looking me up and down like she is really from the ghetto. "I'm here to make sure Mr. Sumpter...none of your business why I'm here! The only man I gotta answer to is Jesus."

That's probably why you ain't got no man! I didn't say that out loud, but I was thinking it. By this time we were at the room's entrance. She pushed me out the way, walks inside, and begins speaking to the bed. I thought she was bugging until I walked over to the bed and saw him. He was small and wrapped in white blankets and sheets. A small face peered through an opening looking like baby Moses on the banks of the river Nile.

"Good morning, Mr. Sumpter." Ms. Johnson said all bright and cheery, and in the same breath hit me upside my head WHAP and continued, "This is Mr. King, he's gonna be coming to check on you, okay?"

When she turned to walk out the room her huge bosom brushed against my elbow. Instinctively I pushed

133

back a little and for a split second our sights met. They communicated more than either of us would say. Then she walked away.

I've been locked up too long!

No one understands the extent of my struggles!

"Good morning Mr. Sumpter. Man, you're so little I didn't even see you." I said without consciously thinking.

He could have the Napoleon complex and been offended by those words. The titty brush threw off my train of thought or I would never have came out with something like that without knowing his demeanor first.

Unfazed by my tactless statement, he beamed a blinding smile at me and returned, in a kind yet dignified manner, "Yeah, I'm a small man," without the slightest amount of sarcasm.

In this instance I'm reminded of Haile Selassie, ruler of Ethiopia for more than 40 years, and descendant of Menelik. Menelik's parents are the Queen of Sheba and King Solomon.

When Haile Selassie was young his name was Lij Tafari. Lij Tafari was a small man and an unlikely candidate to succession to the throne. But his air and mannerism lifted his status far above his competition. And through Lij Tafari the Ras-Tafari faith originates.

In Mr. Sumpters polite assertion, "I am a small man," he articulated eloquently the operative word; Man.

August 28, 2005

I'm visiting the new patient Terrence Sumpter and I'm in awe. He is 37; the same age as me and he looks bad. I don't know how else to describe it. Yet he is at peace. You can see it in his eyes. The whole of his body is decayed except his eyes. They are huge and dark and piercing. It's as if this dude is not looking into my flesh. It's as if he is peering into the essence of my very soul.

"How is your son?" he asked in a soft mild voice.

"Huh?"

I didn't recall telling him about my son. We only spoke briefly yesterday and then I left.

"The little boy that's with you." Then he pointed his slender finger towards the corner.

That's when it dawned on me. This is that room! The room where Woody's patient saw the...the...I felt a cold chill that made me unsure if, in fact, there was something there.

My fears were comforted by Mr. Sumpter's smiling as if he was watching a pot-bellied puppy chasing his tail, and an overwhelming sense of peace covered the room. If whatever he saw is indicative of where he is going, then obviously he's going to a better place. GOD knows best.

August 29, 2005

135

Monday Morning Meeting

I arrived at the meeting a little late. It wasn't a good morning for me. I'm beginning to lose respect for myself. On one hand, I know what I'm doing is wrong, religiously and morally. And on the other hand, it feels so good. It wasn't the actual sensation of sex that's making it so difficult for me to say no. It's the intimacy, the caring, the sharing of each other that goes beyond an orgasm. It's the love. Even if it's not love. Even if it's just knowing that you are wanted.

Ms. Johnson ran the group, and for some reason she appeared more apathetic than usual. As she spoke of Mr. Sumpter I could see that this hit close to home. He has cancer. Which is tragic but I couldn't figure out why this appeared to affect her more than any of other patients she's witnessed on their journey towards Fruition.

Ms. Johnson has worked both Palliative Care and as the Social Worker for lock-up. In both places she has undoubtedly witnessed numerous travesties and injustices. From her conversations, one could easily assume that she has, possibly as a coping device, developed a cognitive dissonance. And this has calloused her sentiment towards prisoners, particularly African Americans. Maybe I've misjudged her.

"Mr. King what's wrong with you today?" Ms. Johnson asked at the groups' conclusion.

136

"I'm seriously thinking of not coming in the afternoons anymore."

"Why? You gettin' burned out?"

"Nah...It's your boy. Your boy be upstairs buggin'."

"What? What boy? Boy what are you talking about?"

"Officer Riggins"

She stopped for a second then said, "Mr. King, don't pay him no mind, he's mad at me, and since he can't do nothing to me he is taking it out on you." She shook her head and finished. "I told you a lot of police don't want this program."

"Okay, but I live here. You know how these racist cops can do. They'll set me up, beat me up, and have me somewhere looking just like Mr. Williford."

She looked as if the thought never crossed her mind and told me to come this afternoon and we can talk more about it because she had a meeting with the administrator in a couple minutes. I reluctantly agreed but had no intentions of returning.

On my way back to 4-2-R I saw Ms. Islam. Wow, that's a beautiful sister and my ideal wife. She doesn't wear traditional Islamic garb. She's more contemporary, classy and stylish, yet everything is loose fitting and covered. Her always matching kymars/head scarves give her a majestic and regal look. Her gait is fluid and swift and her demeanor is friendly yet lady like. She has set the bar for the caliber of woman I want. Seeing her reaffirms my need to stop what I'm doing in E.C.U.

After coming upstairs I signed the list to be seen by her. Partially just to be in her presence and partially of need to talk to somebody. After waiting for a few people to discuss whatever problems they needed her assistance in, she called me in her makeshift office.

"As-Salamu Alaykum."

"Wa alaykum as-salam brother."

Just hearing her say that made me feel better. How could I settle for less?

"Have a seat, brother. How can I help you?"

I explained my situation in E.C.U., at least in part. The part about Riggins and my vulnerability. If he walks up and punches me in the face and pushes the panic button, regardless if I fight back or not, once the response team arrives they are going to beat the brakes off of me. After the beat down I'll be charged with the customary assaulting of an officer. Then, wherever I go in the prison system I'll be labeled and likely beaten again. I've seen it happen too many times before. She looked at me in silence, knowing my words to be true.

"Sister, I just got off of the South Woods Most Wanted list. I'm just getting to the point where I can walk *down the compound without worrying about these clansmen viewing me as a threat." Shaking my head because this is the first that I've consciously thought about it and continued, "I'm just getting comfortable. I got too much time to be fighting a battle that I cannot possibly win."*

Well composed and cognizant that the officer and several inmates are looking back and forth, watching our discourse with suspicious eyes, she still managed to convey her compassion. Slightly trembling, I could see the tears begin to well in her eyes as if she had put a lightning bolt in a head lock and quietly endured the pain and hurt of 400 years of oppression while redirecting that energy into a battery that has been filled beyond capacity since the assassination of Malcolm X.

"Listen Brother, this is all of our problem. We get comfortable."

I didn't see that coming but I remained silent.

Sounding like Assada Shakur she said, "What about the children?", then looked at a paper she pretended to be reading. After a second of agonizing silence, she asked again, in a voice no louder than a whisper, "What about the children? What are we going to do for our children? Brother, if we don't get uncomfortable every now and then, what will we have? Our ancestors had to get uncomfortable for us to have what freedoms we have now. Martin, Malcolm, Marcus, and Muhammad had to get uncomfortable. What will Marte' do?"

Nodding my head, I understood.

"Brother, offer Salatul-istakarah [Prayer of Guidance] and give it to Allaah. Brothers are over there dying...and they need you. We need you."

I swear by Allaah! If one tear had fallen from her eyes, the entire pseudo-macho facade would have been out the door, and I would have cried like a baby.

After settling down for a second to fix my face, I thanked the sister and went to my room for prayer.

With increased faith, I returned to E.C.U. that afternoon. Ms. Johnson met me at the door and took me upstairs. As we approached the desk butterflies filled my stomach like I was about to encounter the neighborhood bully.

"Officer Riggins, I just left a meeting with the administrator. They are very excited about this program. Mr. King will be coming up here every day to visit Mr. Williford. Do you have a problem with this?"

He didn't respond verbally, nor did he say anything about my chain, but he did pat me down. She walked me in the room and I almost hugged her. Instead we both just looked at each other, briefly, but communicating volumes.

"Thank you, Ms. Johnson."

140

"Mr. King, if you're in the right I've got your back."

In an attempt to avoid the intensity of her eyes I lowered my gaze. That was not a good idea. My first stop was her lips, soft and supple. Then, her top heaviness netted my gaze.

She pinched me on my side, bringing me back to reality, and continued, "Boy I ain't losing my job for nobody!"

We laughed for a second, and then she turned around and bopped out of the room.

No one understands the extent of my struggles.

Mr. Williford is improving daily. I would stick my finger or an object in his face to see if I could get his attention. Then I would move it to see if he would follow it. He still has Doll's Eye but they'll travel together more often now. The nurse came in and mentioned that he is still losing weight and showed me more exercises to help protect his muscles from atrophy. I massaged his hand a little but the brother was tired so the full service will have to wait.

September 1, 2005

I ended up staying with Mr. Sumpter longer than usual this morning. His meds softened the pain but didn't put him to sleep so we had the opportunity to kick it a while. He's from Paterson and is down for sales of controlled dangerous substance; drugs. There's nothing surprising about that 85% of everybody in prison is down for drugs or something related to drugs. Drug sales, drug use, robbery to get more drugs, murder to protect yourself from getting robbed for your drugs, or some dumb stuff cause your high off drugs; Reaganomics.

What stood out about his story, to me, is that he was 37 years old and this is his first trip to the pen. Let me break down why this stands out to those who have no prison experience:

First Timers, who have escaped the prison system until the age of 37, don't usually come to jail for drug sales. It's usually for drunk driving, domestic violence, or are sex offenders. An inner-city drug dealer, that age, who has never come to prison, nine times out of ten, is working for the C.I.A., F.B.I., is a major snitch, or all of the above. Yeah I said it! How else you think it gets in the country? In any event, it wouldn't have been small time sales.

Anyway, when he got busted and sat in the county jail they didn't give him medication that he needed to keep his body from rejecting the kidney that he had implanted years earlier. The end result was cancer that is now not just local, its spread through his blood stream.

He had been given a pre-parole program that is similar to house arrest. However, once the cancer hit his blood stream and he needed to be hospitalized, some genius within the system decided they would rather he spend his last days in prison, and had him locked back up.

That's why Ms. Johnson was so moved.

Despite the harshness of the bitter pill that life had forced in his mouth, remarkably, Mr. Sumpter maintained a pleasant demeanor. He's a little Man, but his heart is larger than I could ever imagine having. In this instance, his serenity in the face of suffering reminds me of another man of greatness, the noble Prophet Job. (Peace be upon him) Job had suffered great hardships, loses and afflictions, yet still he continued to praise his LORD. The lesson I get from this is no matter how bad the situation, there is always a Mercy from GOD. If only we could recognize the Mercy there is no need to stress. No need to worry. By stressing and worrying over things you have no control over we are ignoring GODs Grace.

Which of the favors of your Lord will you deny?

September 2, 2005

The next day I pop in bright and early, still high from our interaction the day before, but Mr. Sumpter, who I have nick named Mr. T. because of his toughness, is markedly different. Normally the nurse would come in and give him his medication before she started with the hospital population, but there was a new nurse working and she was extremely slow. I understood. Even seasoned nurses have had difficulties with the volume of patients' medications and it's not uncommon for a person to get the wrong meds. I've seen the affects; not a pretty sight. So she was probably trying to be extra careful.

On the other hand, I could see the pain in Mr. T.'s eyes. And since he couldn't get up like most of the other residents, which were now in a longer line than the one for government cheese, he asked me to check on her and make sure she hadn't forgotten about him.

Feeling a sense of serenity, just from being in his presence, I calmly walked to the desk and said in my humblest voice, "Excuse me nurse, I need your..." She shot me a mini-rock like my breath stunk and turned away like I was a lowly peasant asking for change at the subway station.

I'm not gonna front, all the examples that I just witnessed went smooth out the window, and I felt my blood pressure rise. I felt like Oliver Twist, "Please sir, can I have some more porridge".

Okay GOD, I get it, this is a test. Do you think you will say you believe and not be tested? So I waited patiently for about 4 or 5 minutes without an outward sign of displeasure or impatience.

Then I spoke again, "Excuse me nurse". This time she didn't even turn, she totally ignored me as if I did not exist. Still patient, I smiled, despite the fact that the line was done, and waited a few more minutes, knowing full well that she knew I was waiting for her.

GOD, Grant me the Serenity to accept the things I cannot change; this lady being a jerk; the courage to change the things that I can; how I respond; and the wisdom to know the difference.

Just as I made my silent prayer, another nurse, who is also relatively new and who watched as the events transpired came to my aid. She physically moved the nurse to the side, immediately catching her attention, and asked me how she could help me. I told her about Mr. T and learned that the other nurse thought he was still upstairs. If I had not come he wouldn't have gotten his meds.

Knowing that I helped ease Mr. Sumpter's suffering on the last day of his existence on this physical plane made the minor inconvenience that I experienced with that nurse well worth it.

September 5, 2005

Since Mr. T. has passed I started not to come this morning but I didn't want to hear Ms. Johnson's mouth. Deacon Jim is running the group and now I am really upset that I didn't just stay in bed. He's a good guy. Kind of different, even for a priest and his meetings are so boring that I'd rather be at the dentist. Five minutes in one of his groups and everyone is struggling to hold their heads up. If he could bottle the atmosphere of the class he would make millions!

The death defying Mr. Paterson just came back from the hospital. He's actually been on a vigil twice and just as everyone assumes he is dead, he'll jump right up out the bed like nothing's wrong. He's got all sorts of tubes and picclines in his arms and even in his neck. That's why he had to go to the hospital. He snatched a piccline out of his jugular. Whoa! But dig this, not a drop of blood came out!

After the meeting I decided to pay him a visit before I went back and was glad I did. Clouds of smoke were coming out his door and the closer I got I could hear him saying, "OOw-oow, hot-hot." I rushed through the door and Mr. Paterson had a book of matches, totally inflamed, in one hand and a Slim-Jim, smothered with black soot in the other. I guess he called himself hooking up some fried Slim-Jim. It was hilarious! If he focused in on the Slim-Jim, the book of matches would burn him. "OOw-oow, hot-hot." And if he focused on the matches he would burn his fingers holding the Slim-Jim. "Oow-oow, hot-hot." Then, no sooner than when he removed the meat from the flames, fat sizzling and skin bubbling, he would pop it in his mouth! "OOw-oow, hot-hot." I laughed so hard that I was in tears!

I laughed until the smoke from Paterson's flame broiler set off the fire alarm. This is where my years of hustling on the block came to good use. Often times the police pull people over, not because they witnessed them committing a crime, but because they look suspicious riding by. I slid up out of the room, smooth and fluid, as if

I no idea that Mr. Paterson's room was smoking like a broke stove, and went on my way.

This is my first day staying late up in ECU 2 and it's definitely more loose. I'm seeing things and opportunities that I never really paid attention to before. Sure enough, I see my brother Hofasul, with a mop bucket, busy doing something close to nothing, but different than the day before.

"As-Salamu alaykum." Hofasul greeted with a toothy smile.

"Wa alaykum as-salam," I returned.

"I see you're staying later."

"Yeah, it's good to get away from the 'Fitnah' (troubles) on the block."

"I know that's right, but you have to be careful of the fitnah up here."

Ironically, at that very moment Chocolate walked by and I said, loud enough for her to hear, "Umm-um, Drum sticks, candy yams, sweet potatoes, and cranberry sauce!" She fell out laughing as we both remembered Mr. McKenzie's immortal words.

"That was an inside joke 'Sul'."

"I see...speaking of fitnah, watch that devil broad."

"Who, Dawn?"

"Yeah...that's her."

"Why you say that?"

"Remember the Spainish kid that was working up here?"

Instantly I remembered, the kid that 'shot me rocks' when I first came upstairs to help Mr. Williford.

"Bald head, goatee, and he be arching his eyebrows?"

"Yeah, that's him...you know them poppies be doing that pretty boy shit with their eyebrow."

"Let me catch you on some pretty boy stuff with your eyebrows arched and I'm going straight to the Imam!"

"Yeah, I can see Dr. Yusuuf now. Looking at me talking about, 'Brother for why you do this?' in his Nigerian accent."

We shared another laugh or two then he explained how the Spanish kid was sexin' Dawn for a few months and all of a sudden she flipped on him and got him sent to the hole. She claimed that he threatened her. He had been working here so long that the officer knew it was bullshit but she kept forcing the issue and he had to lock him up. But since they knew him he didn't go to the hole with an ass whipping.

I was struck with the realization that he must have picked up on her digging me and that is why he gave me dirty looks. I wonder if she set him up because of me?

148

"Hey Kingy!" Dawn said as she walked out of nowhere.

"Uh-uh...hey, whats up Ms. Dawn?"

Hafasul spinned off quicker and more quietly than when I left Mr. Paterson's 3 alarm fire.

She looked at me strangely, probably wondering if we were talking about her, then smiled and said, "Can you help me with a patient down the hall?"

"Yeah, sure."

I followed her down the hall and into the same room I was in when I had come from the hospital. The lights were off and the room was empty. Obviously someone else had just been released. We walked by the shower where she pushed me inside, pulled my pants down far enough and began sniffing my private parts. It appeared to turn her on even further. After revving herself into a frenzy she slowly and deeply did her suburbanite private school girl routine.

No one understands the extent of my struggles.

That night, the euphoria of having sex after being deprived for so long was beginning to wear off and my conscience struck me. As I prayed, I truly felt like a hypocrite. It was awful. I began to think of all my ideas of Shangri-La and a Utopian society that I dream of being part of and how the center of my principles of change is responsibility.

Being responsible covers the whole Diaspora of sin, particularly social vices such as premarital sex and adultery. I've contemplated 'Pharaoh's Plan' in-depth; kill the men and take the women and children; live in the trenches, Jim Crows, George Bushs, and Willie Lynches.

I know these are aimed at destroying the family structure so the by-product is easier to manage; to enslave. Yet, like a crack-head with a hundred dollars in his pocket, but no place to lay his head at night, I keep going back to the Crack, literally, to not feel the pain of being a crack-head. The problem is, the pain is only gone while you're hitting it and is intensified upon its return.

This is where I am. This is where I stand. All this time I've been looking for love and affection; longing for sexual gratification. Now that I'm getting it, I'm realizing that I'm really not getting it. And I'm really not feeling it. This ain't living and I cannot continue to live like this.

No one understands the extent of my struggles.

Monday, September 19, 2005

Mr. Williford is doing much better than anyone expected. When I first started coming around he was unresponsive but now, after weeks of trying, he'll actually follow my finger with his eyes. The doctor tried to say that was just instinct but I knew he was conscious inside. He just couldn't move. I understood because I'm in the same position. I am paralyzed, I cannot move, but my mind is fully active. Even though society may think I'm brain dead, useless, in the way, I'm here, struggling to be understood. I am alive.

You say you know why the caged bird sings?

Well I know why the jail bird cries. Feeling vilified, ostracized, useless wings atrophied.

You say you know why the caged bird sings?

Well I know why the caged falcon screams; knowing what it feels like to have the wind under my wings. Tediously pecking away for light. In an abysmal triple stage of night. Misguided...unable to differentiate wrong from right. Surrounded by ignorance, confusion, and mire. Projecting reckless rage while adding fuel to the fire.

You say you know why the caged bird sings?

Well can you tell me why this Alpha Male, inculcated with bad is good, is expected not to fail or end up in jail? We aren't. And no sane person should be surprised. But as soon as I figure out how to use my wings, you will see the Phoenix Rise!

King David was given the Psalms, with verses so powerful that some of its listeners passed out and some even died.

Muhammad was given the Qur'an, with verses so sweet and melodic that without understanding a single word, it has the propensity to cause grown men to cry.

I'm no Prophet. These are merely the words of a caged Man. Wounded, in the dark, striving with all my might just to stand. When it appears that everyone in the world is on the opposing team, why should the African American Alpha Man in a cage still dream?

It's the same reason the caged bird sings.

The physical therapist has laid grip strengthening sponge-like balls in his bed, more for decoration than anything I've seen them do. Sometime he'll squeeze them, let out a sigh, and quickly release them from his grip. That sigh confirmed my suspicions. He's conscious, he can hear me, and he's tired.

I decided that I would toss the soft sponge sphere into his hands to see his reaction. He caught it!

Okay America, I bounced the ball off his head a couple of times to piss him off first. That was just for motivation. Okay and entertainment. After about a week of entertaining me at his expense, he got pissed off enough to raise his right arm about a foot off the bed to catch it. The left hand didn't move as much, but I knew I was on to something.

After a few more catches I could see life in his eyes. He was ready. I went back to that doctor that told me he was brain dead and that his eyes only followed me out of reflex and told him what I had been doing. Well I didn't tell him I was bouncing the ball off his head to get him fired up. But the end justifies the means in the case.

152

He and Nurse Linda were in disbelief. Linda followed me back to the room. When he caught the ball she was so excited she nearly kissed me. 'Yeah Baby,' but instead she showed her appreciation by a not so subtle display of her assets.

No one understands the extent of my struggles!

September 24, 2005

I don't have a main patient in the morning, but I decided to come in anyway. I knew that Dawn wouldn't be in until second shift so I can take this time to clear my head before going to Jumu'ah Prayer.

Green-Eyes is on a vigil, the guy scheduled for duty couldn't make it, his family was coming to visit today, so as soon as Ms. Johnson saw me she asked me to make sure his room is clean.

Actually it was clean, very clean, which indicated that he had not been out of the bed. It was airy, the morning sun burst through his window, and I saw this as a perfect opportunity to study in peace. Emptying the contents of my briefcase I pulled out Napoleon Hill's 'Think & Grow Rich' and went to town.

There is a chapter that speaks about the creative power of men with high sexual appetites and a process of transmuting that energy into success.

Just as I thought of how I could transmute my energies, I was distracted by some pretty toes. I got a *thang for pretty toes. Somebody stepped in the room with light brown, corn-less, bunion-less, blemish free, French manicured feet encased in spaghetti strapped sandals. She obviously knew she had pretty feet and was proudly displaying them by wearing bright blue denims had a three inch cuff that came up to just above her dainty ankles.*

Her button down cotton shirt was printed as if it was an American Flag and she had the sleeves rolled up to the mid-forearm. Just as her feet, her nails were French manicured and if Ray Charles would have felt her wrist he would have known that she is beautiful.

By the time I made it up to her face I was almost embarrassed. Her eyes were filled with grief while mine with lust. It was Green-Eye's mother, and although she is an older woman, she is still very-very-very attractive.

"Boy you should be ashamed of yourself," I heard Ms. Johnson saying in my mind.

I almost laughed at myself as I began to collect my belongings.

We are not supposed to be in the room with the visitors so I was hurrying off.

As I stood, his mom looked me in the face and said, "No, please-please don't go. I can't be alone right now," and gave me a hug.

154

She cried deeply and buried her head in my chest. Her soft hair smelled of Victoria Secret's 'Pear.' No she didn't! Okay Marte'...pull yourself together. If you get hard right now it would be so uncool. Okay, think of something-think of something fast.

"My baby, my baby, my baby," she mumbled.

That's it! I know what to do!

I thought of my momma and all the blood that was racing south quickly made detours elsewhere. Thank you GOD.

But as I began to think of my mother, who too, is still a very attractive woman, I began to realize that she 'could' be my mother; that I could be him. That I could just as easily been laying here dying from H.I.V./A.I.D.S. I've had sex with a lot of women, many of whom indulged in very risky behaviors, and I rarely used condoms.

When I first came to South Woods and had taken an A.I.D.S. test, it took three weeks before they called to tell me the results that would affect me for the rest of my life.

It was count time. That's when everyone is locked in and counted. Our housing unit officer came and told me they want me in the V building right away. Usually when the Administration has some bad news for a prisoner, like a death in the family or something, they'll call them down at count just in case he bugs out.

My mom had pneumonia and was in the hospital. All I could think of was the worst. But once I got to the V Building I realized where I was headed.

My heart raced a 1,000 miles a minute and I silently prayed, "Oh my GOD! Oh my GOD! Oh my GOD! Ya Allaah! If YOU protect me from the 'Package' [A.I.D.S.] I promise to never commit fornication or adultery again. Ya Allaah! You know I'm not a bad guy, please give me another chance. Please!"

I walked in and paced around the waiting area, too nervous to sit. After waiting forty-five minutes for the counselor to call me in, she entered the room.

"Mr. King?"

"Yes"

"Follow me."

She was young and, even though she has a little mustache, she's very attractive and has a beautiful smile. But this time she ain't smiling.

Damn! Damn! Damn!

"Have a seat Mr. King. Sorry to keep you waiting." she says as she opens my folder.

My eyes race across a paper of pure gibberish while she seemed to be prepping me for the news. Oh my GOD.

With an emotionless face she said, "Mr. King, your test was negative."

Oh my GOD! I dropped my head, tears began to well in my eyes, my heart was beating a mile a minute, and I'm near fainting. I'm gonna die in prison. I'm not going to be able to raise my sons. I'm not going to get the chance to make my momma proud... My life is done.

"Mr. King, did you hear what I said?"

As I raised my head the tears were too heavy to come up with my head and rolled down my face. Somehow the word negative seemed negative, which, in my mind meant I was H.I.V. positive.

"Mr. King your H.I.V/A.I.D.S. test is negative."

"Hold up, that means I'm good?" feeling stupid as the words rolled off my tongue.

She smiled, looked in my eyes, and said, "Yeah, you're good."

Flash-forward

"Mr. King!" Ms. Johnson brought me back.

"Uh-uh." I returned, realizing that I have tears in my eyes, and quickly averting my gaze.

She walked around to get a good look at my eyes. I turned the other way, but a tear rolled down my cheek. Green-Eye's mom was oblivious to us both. She needed

157

somebody to hold as she watched her son on his death bed. After releasing her embrace she touched my face gently as if I were her son. She touched my face like she was my mother. She touched my soul forever.

Seemingly energized from our exchange, she walked over to her son and said, "It's okay... momma's here. You can let go now. Momma's here...you can stop fighting."

That was all I could take. I swiftly grabbed my belongings and shot out the door. My emotions were too heavy to mask. Ms. Johnson touched me lightly on the back as I passed; satisfied by answers to questions she had yet to ask.

Later that day.

I was upstairs in Mr. Williford's room when Dawn came in. We exchanged pleasantries, she gave me more oil, and I almost let her kiss me on the lips; almost. I could see the glimmer of disappointment in her eyes and when she reached for my penis and it was not hard, the glimmer turned to panic, or rage, maybe both.

"Dawn, we need to talk."

"What's the matter, Puffy?"

"We can't be doing this no more without condoms."

"What! Why?"

"I'm not trying to come to prison and catch A.I.D.S."

"I don't have A.I.D.S.!"

"Yeah but what about the other guys that..."

"What other guys? I don't mess with other guys!"

"How do you know that I don't have it or herpes?"

"I checked your file before I...you're just trying to get rid of me! I see the way that black bitch looks at you."

"Nah that's not it. Ramadan is almost here...and we can't be doing what we doing."

"We can't be doing what?" her voiced raised.

"Come on Shorty. We've been screwing like jack rabbits all over E.C.U. In fact, we've done it at least once in every room on the left hand side! I'm Muslim. It's bad enough that I'm fornicating but I'm not doing it in the holy month of Ramadan."

"How long is the month of Ramadan?"

If this had been a T.V. show, I would have looked in the camera and said, "You gotta be kidding me."

"It's a month, Dawn."

"A Month! Ah-ah, a whole month! Okay...if that's what you want to do, I guess I understand. I saw how Linda looks at you."

"What?"

159

"Never mind," she murmured and rushed out of the room.

From that point on, every time I was in a room with a nurse she would make it her business to come in to taste the vibe. The crazy thing is men and women speak different languages. Women are much more subtle than men with flirtation. Sometimes we don't understand it but another woman can.

The reverse to that is, damn near anything can be interpreted as a subtle pass. A smile, a gesture, a slight of hand, meant in Dawn's mind, that either I was sexing that person or she was trying to give me some.

I think Chocolate picked up on Dawns insecurities, because her flirtatious manner became more overt than ever just out of spite. I think.

September 27, 2005

Ramadan is almost here and I am feeling more like a Muslim than I have in the last few months. It's sending a general peace and at the same time excitement amongst the community. I've decided that I will skip a few days...spend less time at E.C.U, and when I do come I'll just sweep through in the mornings like I use to, and see Mr. Williford at earlier times. He has other volunteers in the evening so he'll be good.

October 2, 2005

After playing dodge ball from E.C.U. I felt a little safer. I stopped by and paid Mikey a visit. I've known that Mikey is suffering from H.I.V. /A.I.D.S. but it's actuality striking me harder than before. Everyone is excited about him going home. Everyone except him. He confided in me that he's afraid. I asked him why? He said, in a somber yet sobering voice, "Because I'm not the same."

The reality of the matter is none of us are the same. In James Allens' 'As a Man Thinketh', Mr. Allen adequately expresses how we are a product of our thought. Whether we allow seeds of knowledge or the weeds of ignorance into the garden of our minds is up to us. In any event, our actions or inactions will bear fruit. They must come to Fruition.

Most of us come to prison because we got weeds in our garden. Some of us for smoking the weeds from others gardens. Some of us still are. That's how we ended here in the first place. Yet, they are not the same person they were when they came in...they are worse.

While others come in and begin to hoe their plot, plant new seeds/ideas, and begin to produce fruit. But weeds are crafty, if we are not diligently tending our lot, they will return; so will we, to prison.

"Mikey, GOD often challenges us through experience. The Mikey that you are now is not the same Mikey; he is better. Find a way to turn your shortcomings into assets and you will see."

161

"How do I do that?"

"I don't know...that's something you need to first take to GOD. I don't qualify for that position but maybe you can go back into the A.I.D.S. awareness thing. That's what you were doing before you relapsed right?"

"But-but-but...I don't talk the same."

"Yeah, but you get your point across pretty good."

We both smiled and I gave him a hug. I was feeling pretty good for a minute, and then reality struck. I'm such a hypocrite, giving good advice and yet I'm doing something that I know is dead wrong. I'm done! I'm not sexing these girls no more!

As soon as I walked out the door Dawn was standing there with her hands folded. Looking like she was just about to tell me to go outside and get a switch.

"Mr. Marte' King. I haven't seen you in a while, are you hiding from somebody?"

"Hiding from somebody?! I ain't afraid of nothing but GOD, what I look like hiding?"

"Well, don't forget where you're at, maybe you should be?" Then she did a Sybil on me and turned into somebody else. "I got a surprise for you, are you coming in this afternoon to get it?"

"Nah, I got some studying to do," I lied.

"Oh you think your gonna fuck me, take my hard earned money, and kick me to the curb for that black bitch?"

"What?"

"Don't worry, you'll see!" and stormed off.

I came back that afternoon. Dawn was nowhere to be found. I guess since I told her I wasn't coming she had no reason to come up. That was good because the head nurse Linda paid a nice visit. Of course her scrubs were hiked snuggly between her crotch, and if she had panties on, they were definitely thongs because you could see everything. She loves to bend at the waist and show a little breast or squat deeply with her legs far apart to show her print.

I don't even think she consciously does these things. I think they are more so learned techniques of manipulating men that express themselves instinctively. A lot of women do it. If she has large breasts she'll stretch by throwing their hands in the air, poke their chest out, and look the other way so you can Perv. out a little. Y'all know what I'm talking about.

Dawn walked in the room just as Linda did this and went back into a squat. She walked behind Linda and began screaming without sound, "Get out! Get out of the room!"

I could read her lips and I knew she wanted to be unnoticed but I couldn't help asking her, "What?"

163

Linda looked up at her and she shot out of the room. *She's bugging! Even if I was sexing every female in this place, she would have no position to be ordering me out of a room! Who do she think I am; Toby?*

Later on that day, around 5:30 p.m., Officer Mack calls me to the desk at 4-2-R and asks me what I had done. I didn't know what he was talking about. Then he explained that I'm being moved to Phase III, aka 'Three-at-Nam'.

At South Woods, a person doesn't get moved for no reason, and to move to 'Three-at-Nam' meant you pissed someone off. They'll cover it up by saying you've created a problem so when they come and beat the brakes off of you it looks like you are a troublemaker getting just desserts.

Najiullah Musihudeen

October 5, 2005

A new patient has been brought in. Hamza, a new volunteer, was sitting with him and they called me in. People of all faiths need comforting in their final days yet prior to my acceptance there were no Muslim volunteers. Now we have three more. I'm proud to have broken the barrier and setting the precedent.

"As-Salamu Alaykum Abdul Qawi, I've been looking for you for the last few days." the patient said.

Something in the patient's eyes looked familiar, but my mind was preoccupied by my present predicament to place it. I couldn't place him until he reached out his hand. It looked as if it had been smashed and burned while his thumb was torn off and partially reconnected. That's when I realized who it was.

Najiullah Musihudeen was one of my earliest teachers of Islam and though it's been some years, he looks totally different. I could tell by the look in his eyes that he was hurt because I couldn't recognize him but he understood. At least I'd like to believe that.

We caught up on old times and he re-played memories that I still don't recall out in great detail. He's kind of like Mr. Williams but with a lot more Gangsta' to his swagger. He was definitely a Bedouin.

He told me that he had lung cancer. When he said it, I was reminded of his one overt fault. He smoked like a broke stove; Buglers at that! Buglers are loose tobacco that a person rolls up his self. They are probably the scraps that the cigarette companies sweep off the floor.

Tobacco is what spurred the profitability of the TransAtlantic Slave Trade. Many of us are still Slaves and don't even recognize it.

This affected me more because he inflicted himself with the disease. In the eyes of some this is suicide. Outside of the hierocracy that I am showing towards my faith by fornication, I'm taking a bigger risk than a chain

165

smoker by having unprotected sex up in the place all willy-nilly; and the way it's coming at me, I am not the first and likely not the only one.

"Akhi, What is wrong with you?"

"Uh, nothing. Why?"

"Man you are on channel zero. You can't be walking around like this-this is prison! You have to always be on point."

"Yeah, you right?"

"Akhi don't patronize me, make like NIKE and just do it."

"Alright, I will. Salamu alaykum akhi. It was beautiful kickin' it with you but I gotta go. I'm still not finished unpacking."

"Wa alaykum as-Salam. I'll see you tomorrow insha-Allaah"

"Insha-Allaah"

On my way back to 6-2-L, Lo and Behold, Dawn was standing in front of the A building on Phase III, talking real chummy with a high ranking officer that I could have sworn played Chicken Georges' Massa on Roots.

I saw them looking in my direction and just as I passed, Dawn said, "See you tomorrow afternoon Mr. King. I need you to help me move Mr. Williford."

166

If you've ever seen the movie, 'Mandingo', you'd know exactly what I was faced with. Either I continue to be her Sex Slave or she was going to Massa and have them whip my hide, just as she did to the Spanish boy before me.

October 6, 2005

It's the third day of Ramadan and I am not at ease. These pigs are looking at me even stranger than before and my Spider Sense is going bananas. The only reason I'm going to E.C.U. is because it feels a bit safer; and although I know quite a few people over here, I feel like a newcomer.

As I come through the entrance of E.C.U. I exchange pleasantries with a few brothers who work in the hospitals kitchen. This kid named Biz said, "Damn Qawi, for some reason it seems like you're losing your shine." That 'shine' is a glow, a presence, a light that comes from inside and stands out.

"The first week of Ramadan is the hardest. See me in about a week, when I catch my stride, I'll be shining like a black diamond once again." I said, just managing to muster a smile.

As I walked away, all I could think of is T.L.C.'s video to their hit song, 'Don't go chasing waterfalls'. There is a part where a dude catches A.I.D.S. from unprotected sex. He looks in the mirror and his skin is dull and gray. Except in this video, it's not him, it's me looking in the mirror.

"Then he looks in the mirror, but he doesn't even recognize his own face, three letters took him to his final resting place." Don't go chasing waterfalls.

After leaving my I.D. at the desk I waved to a few residents and went to see the brother Najiullah.

"As-Salamu alayum akhi"

"Wa alaykum as Salam brother." he returned without looking. After wiping an eye booger from his face he continued, "Did you bring what I told you to bring?" he asked.

"What?" I asked, not having a clue as to what he was talking about and barely able to discern what he was saying because his voice was so weak.

"Come closer." the agony in his eyes could only be described in one of those ole Negro Spirituals.

As I leaned closer I could see the discoloration of his teeth. His lips were dried and cracked. His body was literally rotting before my eyes. Yet, his mind is as sharp as a tack. Predicting a profound statement like the last words of Mr. Williams, I'm tempted to open my journal and write down what he says.

"What's up big bro?"

In a whisper he asked again, "Did you get what I ask for?"

"Brother, I apologize, I don't remember what you asked for." feeling bad because my problems have caused me to neglect my brother in his last days.

He screamed, "I told you to bring me some Sea Turtle Soup!"

"Some what?"

"Sea Turtle Soup and Green tea."

Figuring out that he was joking, but not getting the punch-line, I grimaced, then smiled and said, "Man you buggin'!"

"No, you buggin', I'm just trying to get your attention. But you are somewhere else."

"I'm going through a few things that's all." actually wanting to tell him but too ashamed.

Thinking of the devil, Dawn walked in the room.

"Hey Kingy, glad you made it." and looked at me like the Chef on Hells Kitchen. "You had a lot of people worried about you." "Hey uh Dawn" I returned, feeling like a chump.

"Hey Mr. Mu-Mu ah, are you okay?"

"Hello nurse Dawn, I have to tell you, you are absolutely the best nurse in the establishment. I appreciate the fact that you are thoughtful, considerate, and consistent."

"Thank you, it's nice to be appreciated some time."

I knew who she was talking about but I wasn't feeding into it. She's stalking and extorting a brother for the schlong and got the nerve to talk about being appreciated.

"Now, Ms. Dawn, where's my Sea Turtle Soup?"

"I-I-I got in trouble already for the Green Tea."

"That's not what I asked you or the subject of this conversation."

"I'm sorry; I'll have to go to another store."

That's it! I've been playing the mister nice guy routine. Time to show her the streets. I left E.C.U. and went back to put my plan together.

That afternoon when I returned to E.C.U. I went straight up to Mr. Willifords room. Dawn was waiting. The room was filled with the smell of Mango Melon lotion that she had rubbed on him prior to my arrival.

"Hey Puffy."

"What's up?"

"You smell that?"

"Yeah"

"It was for somebody else but they act like they don't want it anymore."

"We need to talk."

"Yes we do Puffy. Did you know that you are my only reason for coming to work? I need you."

"What about your husband."

"I told you that we live in the same house but on different floors and he's always trying to turn my daughters against me. Sometimes I feel like just dying. Then you came in my life."

This broad needs a psych.

"Can you please help me with Mr. Johnson down the hall?"

Ivory "One Round" Johnson

September 10, 2005

I've seen Mr. Johnson off and on since I've been over here, but not until I started coming upstairs have I had the chance to enact with him.

A Centurion, Mr. Johnson has to be the oldest prisoner is New Jersey history. An illustrious man who was once a boxer and later a personal chef for individuals thought to be in the mob. Word on the streets is, thirty years ago, his son was suspected of murdering someone.

"One Round" was 70 years old at that time. He took the weight in order to protect his son. Ironically, his son died a year later. Mr. Johnson has been in prison since.

171

He is a wealth of insight and I desperately wish to converse with him about many of the events of the American past that he has lived through. The Marcus Garvey Movement, the Great Depression, World War I & II, Civil Rights Movements and the subtle nuances that would come from someone who has lived through them all. I've tried talking to him but he'd just look at me like I'm crazy.

The way she cared for the old man kind of changed my perspective about her a little. Maybe I've been over-reacting. Maybe my getting moved was a coincidence. Maybe it was just by chance she was talking to that Captain. Maybe she really is looking at me as more than a Mandingo. Maybe she really does care about me. Maybe I'm looking a gift horse in the mouth. I know they say you can't make a ho a housewife, but...I wonder if she would be interested in Islam? Maybe I...nah.

After finishing up with Mr. Johnson I walked down to Mr. Willifords' room to check on him before I leave. After tossing the ball to him a couple of times Dawn walked through the door.

With a look of urgency in her eyes and voice she said, "Hey Puffy, we have to hurry." then dropped down on her knees. "Keep a look out because I think that runner is watching me."

Before I realized I was messing up, she was bobbing for apples so good I forgot about everything else. My knees began to buckle, my toes curled, and I had to grab the wall as she swallowed every drop and wouldn't stop. In the middle of the second round she stood, turned, bent over, and stuck it in, in one fluid movement.

Okay, if this what you want? I'ma give you what you came for, surgery with the chainsaw. I gripped the sides of her booty cheeks so hard I could see my hand prints outlined in red around her milky white flesh and purposely dug harder and deeper than ever before.

She started biting on a towel like a bit in a horse's mouth to restrain her from screaming. I knew she was loving it because she was so wet I could feel her warm juices on my scrotum. That's when I put my hands on her shoulders, bent her back like a slinky and dug in as far as I could go and started grinding against the gristle.

As I released my second load my body convulsed so hard that the reality of what I have done came crashing on my conscience like a ton of bricks. I just blew my Fast!

If that wasn't bad enough, when I pulled myself out of her a huge clump of blood plopped out and landed right inside my pants. She apologized and quickly attempted to clean me up.

I was traumatized. My walk back to the housing unit was long and arduous. I felt so small I could have drowned in a glass of milk. I felt so low I could have been stepped on by a roach. And I'd never been more disgusted in my life.

173

I hadn't told anyone about what Dawn and I were doing. I couldn't, that would be suicide. But now, even though I didn't know my new roommate, I needed to talk to someone.

After I poured my heart out, Ric, my bunky, looked at me and said with a cheerless voice, "You know if you guys get caught she's going to scream rape?"

"What?"

"Dude, you are a Ward of the State, she is in a position of authority over you. If she gets caught fucking you she can go to jail."

"What?"

"Dude, it's either you or her, who you think it's going to be?"

Without saying another word I went to the shower and scrubbed myself raw and prayed for forgiveness. I'm in a catch 22, I cannot win. If I keep screwing her I will not be able to live with myself. If I don't, I can't live in South Woods.

That night I had a dream that I robbed someone but only got a safe. The safe was filled with jewels but I didn't have the combination. I used a sledge hammer and a blow torch trying to open it. I started using a chainsaw and somehow cut my hand off. In a panic, I rushed to the hospital, and tied a belt around my arm to stop the bleeding. I fell asleep and woke up in a panic because I

174

forgot to bring my hand. So I went back home to get my hand. It had been a couple of days now and I realized that it was probably too late to have it reattached. I was extremely saddened and I felt pains in my hand that was no longer there. In tears, I pick my lifeless hand up and put it back in the place where it once was. Amazingly I could feel and move it as if it were still attached. I went to the hospital and they sewed it back on.

When I woke up I understood what the dream meant. I had severed the hand of righteousness. But GOD is Oft Forgiving, Most Merciful. Its not time to give up, its time to till my garden.

October 18, 2005

I went into to see Najiullah, who by now had scared all the other volunteers away, and enjoyed his company. He has a rugged and sometimes harsh exterior, but he's not a bully. He was raised in an era where he had to be that way. So it is difficult for him to tolerate softness. At this juncture in my life, that is exactly where I needed to be; I'm on the battlefields.

I got the opportunity to pick his brains on the history of Atlantic City's street gangs, the Salaams and the Abdullah's. I had heard stories but many varied and none were as detailed as this; and it actually explained why I'm having such a hard time getting along with one of gangs earliest leaders. A man who has a charismatic affect on people, and who has the capacity to be a catalyst for positive social change; a man with whom I've studied for years now; a man who is my greatest antagonist.

For the next few weeks, even with increasingly stronger and more overt threats I refused her advances. I was able to resist her but...I-uh, for some reason Dawn believes that I had taken interest in uh... did I mention that E.C.U. is kind of big? In any event, she managed getting me moved again. This time back to Phase II, but this time, 4-1-R.

This tier is as segregated as the Jim Crow South, and terrorized by an officer known as 'Hot Pot Ernie'. They call him that because he has an affinity for taking peoples metal hot pots.

He's believed to be one of the 'Good ole Boys'. His uncle works this tier first shift and his mother works here too. I'm not sure if he's 311 or not. But I do know that one whole row behind the officers desk on the flats of 4-1-R has nothing but white boys. This is New Jersey! Blacks and Latino combined make 23% of the population on the streets and 90% of the prison population. There is no way of having an entire row of whites without it being engineered; and all of them have three or four metal hot pots. They also had the drugs. I wonder where they get them from?

I knew the set-up was soon, and at the point where I'm tired of the games.

Okay. I'll be your huckleberry.

November 5, 2005

Mr. Johnson just got back from the hospital and is as cantankerous as ever. It's close to 70 degrees outside so I figured I'd take him out for some air. After facing him towards the sun I pulled a chair up beside him. There is no breeze, the skies are clear, and if you look up and pretend to not see the razor wire fences and spotlights oddly shaped like swastika's you feel almost free; as free as you could ever be, for freedom is not something that can be given or taken away without your consent. Freedom is a place from within...a place where peace resides.

November 6, 2005

Mr. Johnson is now on oxygen. They put a mask on his face but he just keeps pulling it off. If he don't want it, I'm not gonna keep force it on him. They also keep specialized mittens on his hands so that he cannot pull the feeding tube out his stomach or scratch people. He's got an iron grip and if he pinches you with those old man nails he'll draw blood.

He might be able to pinch but if you get close enough he'll punch you in the face. He almost got me once. I dipped it and he grabbed my arm and started biting me ferociously. I screamed for a second then realized he has no teeth. Fortunately no one was there to bear witness.

November 7, 2005

Today is the very first time I've ever heard Mr. Johnson articulate a complete sentence and it is yet another occurrence that I shall never forget.

I was on my way to see Mr. Williford and heard some commotion going on down the hall. Being nosey, (you know how we do) I poked my head in Mr. Johnson's room and unwittingly volunteered myself to help Chocolate give him a sponge bath. Of course I wasn't sponging anything below his neck. My job was to hold him down, as much as possible, and stop him from kicking and swinging.

He was calm, at first, as long as what she washes is on the top side of his body. [Yeah Baby] But with the slightest movement of his body, to the left or right, no matter how gentle, causes him to scream in sheer agony. So as soon as she attempted to turn him over to wash the bottom all hell broke loose. To be honest with you, I don't know if he's really in pain or just doesn't want to be moved. But then again, I'm not 100 years old.

Chocolate lifted Mr. Johnson's left leg with expertise and grace and he screamed, sounding just like the 3,000 year old Mummy, "AAAHHhh-AAAHHhh!" Undaunted by his cries, Chocolate leaned him to the right side and he screamed even louder, "AAAHHhh-AAAHHhh!" he was literally as stiff as a board.

Now he's pissed! He couldn't throw jabs because I had him pent but he was pinching the crap out of me with *those old man nails. She had to lower the safety rail to get closer. He was doing his best to kick her. She was obviously familiar with his routine, I was not. Somehow his leg got caught between the bed and the safety rail.*

After all this time that I have been coming around, this is the first time that I have ever heard him articulate a sentence. Sounding just like one of the old hecklers that sit in the balcony on the Muppet Show, Mr. Johnson screamed, "AAAHHhh-AAAHHhh You're-you're-you're breaking my leg!"

I laughed so hard I was no mo' good!

I laughed so hard that Chocolate started laughing.

We laughed so hard that it put a smile on Mr. Johnson's face; another first.

I once saw a program on PBS where orphaned infants and crack babies were paired with the elderly. It showed that the babies did better when they were exposed to tactile sensations; to be touched, to be held, to be spoken to with compassion. Interestingly, they found that not only did the babies fare better, but so did the elderly. Conversely, to isolate a person, to deny him the ability to touch, or to hold, or to show compassion is another form of torture.

Being in prison is already a hardship. Most of us lose contact with family and loved ones and the emotional distancing is debilitating. I can only imagine what it would be like to be the oldest inmate, possibly in the history of prison, with no one to love. No one to talk to that is even remotely close to his age. No one to trust. No one to touch. Nobody!

We, as a nation, have to find better ways to care for our aging society. It is our duty. As Americans, it is our collective responsibility.

I started applying these techniques to Mr. Johnson by rubbing his scalp. He was in heaven, and I soon learned that it was the only way I could calm him down when he had his fits.

Chocolate finished washing and began bending over, at the waist, to pick up her supplies that were all over the floor. Mr. Johnson's 100 but he ain't dead. So I stood behind his bed, gave the old man a scalp massage, and we watched the show as Chocolate did her bend and stretch routine.

Drum sticks, candy yams, sweet potato pie, and cranberry sauce!

November 8, 2005

They removed the oxygen mask from Mr. Johnson and attempted to stick tubes in his nose. Yall know that ain't work well at all.

I saw Dawn cleaning a room down the hall and making her way closer to here, but before she got too close I high tailed it out of there.

November 12, 2005

Mr. Johnson is in the hospital. They say he was bleeding through the mouth and nose, but he's still a fighter. One Round Johnson, throwing punches til the end.

Dawn walked in and my stomach began to flip. I shouldn't have ever done the nasty with her. The crazy part is I had all the warnings in the world but thinking with the other head I didn't recognize them until it was too late.

"I see what you're doing around here."

"What are you talking about Shorty?"

"Don't call me Shorty, I heard you call that black bitch Shorty?"

Had she been eavesdropping on my conversations?

"I'm from D.C., we call everybody Shorty."

"Oh, ah, well Ramadan is over." she said with a sly smile

"Listen Shorty, I told you I'm not doing nothing without condoms."

Just like Sybil, she transformed into another alter ego and snapped, "Did you tell her to bring a condom?"

She is really playing me like a chump. If she was a man I would be punching her in the face about now! Enraged but cognizant of my surroundings I returned, "What? Listen...after all this bullcrap you've put me through, do really expect me to..."

"It's because I'm white?"

"What?"

This was the third personality in less than a minute.

"I know you Muslims don't like white people."

"That's the Nation of Islam. I'm a Sunni Muslim and there are millions of Caucasian Sunni Muslims."

"Huh?"

"The religion of Islam is not based on color, or nationality, nor was it sent to one race. It's a way of life that's for everybody. And in every country of the world you will find a thriving Muslim community. In fact, Spain was a Muslim country for nearly 700 years and they're white."

"How come I never heard that in school before?"

"The same reason we are still taught that Christopher Columbus discovered America."

"He did...didn't he?"

Chocolate and another young African American nurse walked in the room. Dawn looked up briefly like a lone lioness outnumbered by hyena and quickly scurried away before being injured. Of course they laughed and I knew that somehow I was going to pay for that.

November 16, 2005

Hot Pot Ernie is on my trail. He told me that if he finds anything in my room that I'm not supposed to have he's going to lock me up. That's no surprise. But for him to go out of his way to tell me this meant someone had put me back on the South Woods Most Wanted list. Once you're on that list, even if you're squeaky clean, you got drama. I know how Hot Pot gets down. After destroying my personal property I'll end up with a mystery shank in my room or something. I gotta get off this unit fast.

I also have to change my routine up a little. Go to E.C.U. at different times in case the hit squad wants to snatch me up on my way and throw me in the property room; no cameras, no witnesses, and beat me to death.

So I waited until second shift to go to E.C.U. It was time for me to speak with Hafasol. I knew I could trust him and I figured I'd get some good advice. When I got there I tried to talk to him but he was too busy to sit still long enough for me to break it down.

All he said is, "You can take tops and I'll take bottoms."

"What?" I asked, confused as ever.

"Okay, I'll take top and you can take bottoms. It doesn't make me a difference. You my brother! Don't any of these broads mean anything to me." and walked away.

Is everybody in this place crazy or is it just me?

It was getting late and I was ready to go but I still couldn't get to Hafasol and tell him what's going on. Now I'm wondering what he meant earlier. They had him working in an area were the dialysis machines were set up. I'm not authorized to go there without escort, so I walked the hall and tried to gain his attention. Nurses Joyce and Chocolate were getting on the elevator for their break.

"Excuse me Ms." I said as the door was shutting

Chocolate stuck her hand in the door to prevent it from shutting and asked, "Whats up?"

"I need you to get Hafasol for me. He's in the back and..."

She abruptly jumped off the elevator as if she didn't want to go in the first place. Joyce looked at me, confused, as the elevator door shut.

Chocolate kindly escorted me through a door right next to the elevator. I nervously surveyed the area and noticed that the officer was not at the desk so I slid in as quickly as possible to avoid detection.

184

It was dimly lit, quiet, and spooky, a good scene for a scary movie; and as if scripted, Hafasol stepped out from a corner with a toothy grin. I followed more closely behind Chocolate than I realized, so when she stopped abruptly, and turned to face me, I could feel the softness of her femininity. She turned, looked up submissively, amorously and asked, "What you want?" Drumsticks, candy yams, sweet potato pie, and... No one understands the EXTENT of my struggles!

November 17, 2005

It was a beautiful morning. The air was crisp and I was feeling great. When I got in I noticed one of the kitchen workers that had been eye balling me lately posted in one of the 'sweet spots'. Sweet Spots are places where you can lay your Mack down on one of the officers or nurses without drawing attention. He was around my age but had long hair like one of these young boys but today he looked very different.

When I come in I usually take my khaki state shirt off and sport a long-john top with the 'Wife Beater' underneath. Not too tight but form fitting enough to catch an eye or two. Hey if you got it... Even if I have on rags they will be clean and pressed. Even in prison I maintain my hygiene and take special care to have my head clean shaven and my mustache and goatee manicured.

Anyway, this guy is now sporting a bald-head, has on a tight long-john top, and looks cleaner than he ever

185

has before. Swagger Jacking is a form of flattery. But he's not like me, like me, no he's not like me.

When I showed up and flexed he was vexed, the conversation abruptly changed its context, and I smiled, knowing this was no contest.

"Good morning Mr. King"

"Good morning Dawn" I returned with the cheeriest of smiles.

The kid she was talking to shot me a rock but he couldn't beat me so I really didn't care. This was a good thing. If I can manage to keep her as a friend, I can still get oils and not have to do it to her. After the customary slight nod of the head, I gave him enough direct eye contact for him to avert his sights and bow his head in subconscious submission, and kept it moving.

I went to look out after my new patient and about three minutes later Dawn walked in the room and handed me a bottle of oil and said, "Hey Puffy, Ramadan is over, meet me in the room down the hall."

She caught me off guard with that and my little head spoke before I had the chance.

"When?"

Her face lit up like the Fourth of July.

"Five minutes."

"Alright."

186

*As she stepped out the room reality struck. Marte',
you are bugging! You are about to open up a brand new
can of bullcrap. Think Marte', think, think.*

*At that moment, the officer walked over and asked
me if I could help him. This was extremely odd, bordering
on Divine Intervention, because he had never done this
before. And the timing was perfect because the windows of
opportunity for conjugal visits are slim. If I prolonged my
helping of the officer, I could save face and she'll have no
need to be mad at me because it ain't my fault. GOD is
good!*

*After 45 minutes of cleaning and talking to the
officer about nothing. I headed to the rendezvous locale,
feeling safe. The floors of the hall were particularly glassy
and I thought of how much it would cost to maintain
floors like this on the streets. As I walked in the room I
noticed Dawn bent over at the waist and performing
fallacio on 'Mini-me' with no hands. Looking like she was
bobbing for apples.*

*Before I could turn around he spotted me and
quickly pulled his pants up. Dawn pretended to be picking
something up off the floor.*

"Pardon Self" I said.

*"Oh-nah...you good, I-I-I was just helping her with
the...ah" then he shot out the room.*

*Dawn was looking nervous and strange with sweat
on her forehead and above her lips.*

187

"Listen here Shorty, that's my bad, you should have said something and I would have looked out for yall."

"What took you so long?" she changed the subject

"What?"

"You had me down here waiting for you so I asked him to help me fix the bed. That's all we were doing."

"What? Listen Dawn, you are good peoples...we are just friends."

She looked at me like I was crazy but I guess she figured the gig was up and handed me a small bottle of oil that she picked up at English Town.

"Are you coming this afternoon?"

"Nah" I answered and walked out the room.

As I walked down the hall I saw Mini-me next to the officers' desk as if he were waiting for me. He had a tough-guy look on his face like he had a problem and motioned for me to follow him outside.

I swiftly followed him with extra pep in my step. This noticeably made him uneasy. He's use to seeing the good humble Muslim and he may have taken kindness for weakness.   Standing dangerously close, and slightly towering over him, I asked, "What's good?"

"Ah-ah, what's up with you and Dawn?" he humbly asked.

I smiled, shrugged my shoulders and said, "The same thing that you are doing."

Dawn is a compulsive and convincing liar. She lies so much that I think she believes herself, and by the look of hurt in his eyes, I see that he must have believed her too. I thought he was going to cry. I didn't care as long as she was bringing the oils, and afterwards it didn't matter. He was just figuring it out. She had been telling him that the reason she would spend so much time with me is because I was spying on her and she was trying to throw me off her tracks. It didn't make sense to him but sex and gifts to a man in prison can cloud your logic. Trust me I know.

After venting and getting his emotions in check he said with psuedo-sincerity," You get what you can get and I'll get what I can get and we'll leave it at that."

"Brother, I don't even.."

"Yo, I gotta roll, I think she saw us talking." and he scurried off.

Why is he so scary?

I went to check on a patient and Dawn was in the room making up the bed.

"What's up Dawn?"

She acted like she was busy then answered, "Hello Mr. King." in a very cold voice.

"Listen Dawn, I'm not mad at you, you're doing me a favor. Those oils you give me are helping a lot. I'm even in a position where I'm able to send things home to my sons. That means a lot to me."

She turned and smiled a little, then looked out the door as if she was expecting someone.

"I appreciate you bringing me in stuff and I don't have a problem paying you. We just can't be doing what we been doing."

This time she turned around and her pasty white skin was crimson red.

"Are you threatening me?" she screamed

"No, I'm just saying we can't be..."

"ARE YOU THREATENING ME!" she screamed at the top of her lungs.

Uh-oh, she's trying to hit me with the same move she put on poppi!

I did my best impression of Michael Jackson and did the Moonwalk straight out the room. Normally around this time of day the halls are packed and two or three officers would be at the desk. By the grace of GOD nobody heard her. No one was in the hallway nor were any officers at the front desk. GOD is good!

If the wrong crew heard this white woman, screaming in distress, because of me, they would beat me worse than Rodney King. [no relation] They would have beaten me like beat Emit Teel, and probably get away with it like they got away with murdering him.

I made it to my patients' room to get my belongings and get out as soon as possible. She followed behind me as if nothing had ever happened and began helping him. I wasn't falling for the banana in the tail pipe. I left that room, walked to the front desk, grabbed my I.D., and went straight back to 4-1-R. I quit! That was too close. As much as I hate to admit it, I was contemplating checking in to P.C. [Protective Custody] Also known as Punk City. The ultimate humiliation!

An emergency response team of officers ran on our unit and straight at me. Oh my GOD! They ran straight passed me and I felt a little ease until I saw them headed to my room. My heart was pounding at 100 miles a second but by the Grace of GOD, the Sgt. wasn't one of the 'good ole boys'. Knowing they were looking for me I approached him first.

"What's up King?"

"What's up?"

"Man, do you know why I'm here?" looking disappointed.

"I think so."

He showed me the charge and told me that if the prosecutor of the county chooses to, I could be charged with Terroristic Threats and have time added to my sentence. I told him that I didn't threaten anybody and that I was being set up. He said, "It's basically your word *against hers and who do you think they are going to believe?" He had me handcuffed and taken to the hole.*

As I sat in the hole I began to ponder over the events that led to this. You know how we do; after the fact. I also thought about the program and how much I would miss it. It's a trip because when I was young, running the street, and feeling invincible, I thought as little about death as possible. I lived life in the moment and didn't care about anything else.

In Buddhism tradition, the Universal Meditation of Death is considered one of the most powerful methods of changing human behavior. Because nothing will force you to take your life into account quicker than realizing the fact that you are mortal.

My experiences at Palliative Care have definitely helped me changed my behaviors in ways that I didn't even realize I needed to change. Sure I've shed a tear or two, but it was worth it.

I've learned lessons from each and every person I cared for. Mr. Williams taught me that I am a Man no matter where I am and no one can take that from me.

Mr. Green taught me to strive for the truth until my last breath. Mr. McKenzie showed me that no matter how bad the situation may appear there is always room for laughter.

Red taught me that beneath our uniforms (i.e. race, religion, or rationale) we are all the same.

192

Mr. Lopez showed me that Death is not necessarily a bad thing. Alameen taught me dignity in distress.

Colonel taught me that no matter how little you have you always have something to give.

Najiullah taught me that just being able to pray is a blessing. Mr. Sumpter taught me patience in affliction.

Green Eyes showed me the end result of playing Russian roulette with my penis; and how my reckless disregard affects the ones I love.

Momma, *for all the heartaches worries and pains that I've ever put you through, I apologize.*

To my sons Mar'quan and Bukhari, *for not being physically there for you to aid in your growth towards Manhood, learn from my mistakes so you don't have to go through what I am going through to learn how to be a Man. Constantly reexamine yourself and the motives for your actions because everything that you do has a price. All of our actions come with a cost, and some of the things that we think we gotta have come at too high of a price. You will make mistakes! Once you recognize your mistakes, forgive yourself for transgressing against your own self, and strive not repeat them. Life is forgiving and wherever there is Life, there is hope. Just as the song goes, "We fall down...but we get up! For a Saint is just a sinner who stood up." Last but certainly not least, "GOD specializes in making the impossible possible." HE makes*

193

paths when there appear to be none. So never give up your faith in GOD.

When I turned my back on GOD, HE never turned HIS Back on me. During the time period I felt trapped, with no one to turn to, and unworthy of turning to GOD, HE was there. When I was a straight-up hypocrite and deserving of HIS Wrath, HE Protected me without my knowledge.

I didn't know that early that morning Dawn came in and had already set the stage for my trap. I guess she figured if she couldn't have me, nobody else would. She told the officer that I was becoming unduly familiar with her and that I should be admonished and instructed that I should refer to her as Mrs. Dawn.

She wanted me to meet with her where there were no witnesses but can be heard by all. She wanted to punish me for my disobedience. But as GOD revealed in Isaiah 54:17 "No weapon forged against you shall prosper..."

GOD sent the same officer who Dawn was setting the stage with; to come asked me for my help during the most opportune time for her to do it. Then when she did do it HE put a covering over everyone's sight and hearing to protect me. Instead of one of the 'Good ole Boys' HE sent a Sgt. to come lock me up that knew me and my character. Before all this happened, HE had me moved into a room with someone who was able to give me some sound advice. Ric told me to safeguard myself. So instead of throwing

194

away the dozens of love letters and cards she was sending I began to keep them.

This, through the Grace of GOD, saved me. This was more than my word against hers, and after one look at the handwriting on these letters and the handwriting on the bogus charge she wrote, it was obvious that they were written by the same person.

A few days later I was given a polygraph to prove my innocence and passed with flying colors. I guess the truth can set you free. They dismissed the charges that she filed against me and she was arrested and charged with Sexual Assault. The charges were eventually dismissed, and though I don't wish prison on her, she needs help, and I can't help but to wonder what would have happened to me if the situation was reversed. If I had threatened, stalked, and extorted her for sex, and when my advances failed I set her up, what do you think would have happened to me?

Answer: I'd be on the News and under the jail.

Is it because I'm Black?   Is it because I am a Man? Or is it because I'm a Black Man?

"An injustice anywhere is a threat to justice everywhere."

February 26, 2009

7:00 a.m.

A211 ACSU East Jersey State Prison

I just completed writing this book, and though it has been several years since its occurrence I am still suffering from it; mentally, psychologically, and physically.

However, every hardship, every difficulty, and every tribulation comes with a Seed of benefit. What I learned from Dawn is everything that glitters is not gold. Everything that is bought should not be sold. And it is better to till the soil and plant my seeds in fertile ground if anything good is to come to FRUITION.

So what happened to you afterwards?

I got shipped out of South Woods, Rahway, Bayside, and I eventual ended up in one of the most dangerous prisons in the country, the infamous Northern State. Where there are more gang member per capita than South Central L.A. Where even some of the police are banging. Where someone is getting stabbed up at least once a week. Where there is so much wrong going on that it left just enough room for a brother doing right to squeeze through door that are impregnable in other places. I began teaching business classes and what I found is that even those who are considered the most dangerous amongst us want better. We want more. We want change.

With the help of Imam Musa Abass I was given a forum to begin teaching business classes and testing my strategies in the chapel area of Northern State.

Then, through the assistants of Mr. Rey Perez, I received permission from the Head of the Education Department of Northern State Prison to begin having classes in the school area. A major feat, and though I am not longer there, the classes are still in effect.

Constantly striving to transform my misfortunes into assets, I've utilized Ohio University's scholastic tutelage, insights from magazines like Black Enterprise & Entrepreneur, combined them with my knowledge of prison and the pedagogies that lead to it, my accumulated experiences, insights, and aspiration and created a program for prisoners called RePENT.

[Recidivism Prevention thru ENtrepreneurial Training]

RePENT **(Recidivism Prevention thru Entrepreneurial Training)** *is amalgamation scholastic, therapeutic, and motivational/inspirational teachings that mold the innate aptitudes that the incarcerated have for taking risk and transform them into legitimate entrepreneurship.*

I hope you enjoyed reading my works and look forward for more to come. I hope that in some way you look and prison and prisoners differently. America, we are all in this boat together. America, land of chattel Slavery, Genocide, Institutional racism, has changed to the point that we now have an African American President. We too, behind these walls, are Americans, and **WE TOO CAN CHANGE.**

I don't claim to be a writer. I'm an Entrepreneur who can write, and am utilizing my talents to gain capital to bring RePENT to FRUITION. I appreciate your support and welcome your comments or suggestions.

All praise is due to GOD, through whom all things are possible. While watching Tyler Perry on Oprah, he gave an account of how he, before stardom, was watching Oprah and she said, "Writing is a catharsis", and this changed his life forever. After looking up the word catharsis, I realized that that was exactly what I needed,

198

and I was inspired to write this book. Thank you to both Oprah and Mr. Perry.

Other special thanks go out to Steve Harvey. I listen to your messages regularly, and find you are a constant source of inspiration. Unlike some African Americans, who have used their celebrity status to bash and further the negative stigmas and prejudices against the incarcerated, you consistently encourage us with love while enforcing the fact that we MUST do better.

To my brothers and sisters who are incarcerated, it's time to step our game up, Obama is the president, and we have to do better.

Lastly, to the American public. We are living in times where people are living longer. Many of our elderly will need caring for and it is not satisfactory for us to pack up our parents and grandparents and ship them off to some nursing homes with no regard; or just to forget about the ones who have no family.

America, our freedoms come with a price; a responsibility. That includes collective responsibility to each other. This is the only way we can actualize Dr. King's dream. Regardless of sex, race, creed, or color, we have a collective responsibility to each other; for each other.

America let's not forget about our elderly who have paved the way for us to become who we are. And let's not neglect the numerous brothers and sisters dying in hospice *programs across this Country and in prisons. They too, are Americans.*

America, I did it! I finally made it out. After serving 10 years, three years of which I continuously petitioned the Courts to grant me a change of custody to a Drug Program, Judge Garofolo granted my motion and I am now in the John Brooks Recovery Center in Atlantic City, NJ. While here, I was fortunate enough to meet a powerful sister who is the CEO of a non-profit called RAFHA, Inc. Her name is Mrs. Laura Griffin-Greenwood, MHS. *www.Rafhaina.com*, e-mail: *Lauravan123@aol.com* She is doing some fabulous work through Gender Responsive Services for Girls. She has adopted my program and offered me a position as lead coordinator in re-entry services and is partnering with me to jumpstart RePent into Fruition. Proceeds from the sale of Fruition are going towards RePent.

Made in the USA
Charleston, SC
01 September 2011